THE HIBBERT LECTURES 1959

DARWIN AND BUTLER

Two Versions of Evolution

THE HIBBERT LECTURES 1959

DARWIN AND BUTLER

Two Versions of Evolution

Basil Willey

Fellow of Pembroke College
King Edward VII Professor of English Literature
in the University of Cambridge

HARCOURT, BRACE AND COMPANY

NEW YORK

PREFACE

WHEN the Hibbert Trustees did me the great honour of inviting me to give these lectures, I had already been asked to arrange my thoughts, for another occasion, on 'Darwin's Place in the History of Thought'. Casting about for a suitable theme for the Hibbert Lectures, and bearing in mind that 1959 marked the Centenary of the *Origin of Species*, I came to the conclusion that 'Darwinism' would be an appropriate topic. I ought perhaps to have reflected that if the Centenary suggested Darwin to me, so it would also to scores of other people, most of them far better qualified than I. So many articles have been written, and lectures delivered, on this subject during the past twelve months, that I am afraid my remarks may now seem like pancakes warmed up for Ash Wednesday. However, I propose to treat Darwinism not merely as a chapter in the history of biological science but as an influence powerfully affecting the thoughts and feelings of the last century, and indirectly of our own time. And I propose to widen the survey still further, by discussing another nineteenth-century figure linked with Darwin in the relation of antipathy, Samuel Butler. These lectures may appear to be yet another, and the most flagrant, instance of my inveterate propensity to raid other people's preserves. I am sorry if this is so, and I can only offer a few lame excuses: one, that for thirty years I have been living in the shadowy border-country between literature and the 'history of ideas', and am too old now to shift my quarters; another, that the *Origin of Species* has been truly described as the last major work of science written to be read and understood by the common reader; and lastly, that however we may choose to define the term 'literature'—and it is not so easy to define as is often supposed—Samuel Butler, at least, belongs to it.

Pembroke College, Cambridge
1959

CONTENTS

Preface   *Page* v

Lecture I: Charles Darwin: his Theory and its bearing
             upon Religion   9

Lecture II: Evolution before Darwin; Darwin through
             contemporary eyes   32

Lecture III: Samuel Butler and Darwin   60

Lecture IV: Butler and Religion   87

Index   115

LECTURE I

Charles Darwin: his Theory and its bearing upon Religion

IT is a truth universally acknowledged in the textbooks, that about a hundred years ago something tremendous happened in the history of thought. Three great explosions took place in rapid succession which rocked the fabric of Christendom and sent believers scuttling for shelter. The first was the *Origin of Species* (1859), the second, *Essays and Reviews* (1860), and the third, Bishop Colenso's *The Pentateuch and the Book of Joshua Critically Examined* (1862, and onwards to 1879). The last two have passed into the limbo of dead controversies, but Darwin is still a potent name. What was there in his book to cause so much excitement? Perhaps I should first, in the fewest possible words, repeat the story of its birth, and then try to tear out the heart of its argument.

Charles Darwin (1809-82), when a schoolboy, had this said to him by his father, the prosperous Dr Robert Waring Darwin of Shrewsbury: 'You care for nothing but shooting, dogs, and rat-catching, and you will be a disgrace to yourself and all your family'—words which must surely rank high in the list of famous unfulfilled prophecies. They do, however, hint at something essential in the boy's make-up: his distaste for school-books and his penchant for open-air pursuits. Of his schooling at Shrewsbury School under the famous headmaster Dr Butler (grandfather of Samuel Butler), he afterwards wrote that nothing could have been worse for the development of

9

his mind, as the curriculum was 'strictly classical'. Believers in classical education (if any such still exist) need not be unduly perturbed by this pronouncement, for Darwin meant little more than that he happened to be a dunce at languages. Two years at Edinburgh University as a medical student convinced him that his repugnance for dissection and the operating theatre would prevent him from ever being a successful physician, and accordingly his father sent him to Cambridge to be made into a clergyman. He quite liked the idea of being a country parson, and had then no doubts about 'the strict and literal truth of every word in the Bible'. Although he read and admired Paley's *Evidences*, and studied *Pearson on the Creed*, the serious business of his Cambridge life was collecting beetles. And the two books that influenced him most deeply were the extra-curricular *Personal Narrative* of Humboldt, and Herschel's *Introduction to the Study of Natural Philosophy*. These books aroused in him a passionate desire for travel and discovery—a desire which was gratified, beyond all expectation or likelihood, by his appointment as naturalist on H.M.S. *Beagle*. He set sail in December 1831, and was away for five years.

Of the voyage of the *Beagle* this is not the place to speak, except to say that for Darwin those five years were by far the most important period of his life and determined his whole career. It was during those years, on the high seas, in South America, among the Galapagos Islands and the coral reefs, that he formed his lifelong habits of concentrated observation and patient reflection, and collected the data from which, after twenty years of brooding and further intensive work, he finally drew his famous hypothesis. The geographical distribution of the creatures of South America, and the geology of that continent (illuminated by the reading of Lyell's *Principles of Geology*), had given him the first glimmerings of his great idea. On his return to England, he first spent five years accumulating every conceivable fact which might have any bearing on the origin of species. Only then, like a true Baconian (it is odd that one of the main charges against the *Origin* should have been that it had *not* been composed on Baconian principles)—only then did he allow himself to speculate on his findings. The glimmering idea had brightened into a wild surmise, and finally dawned into full conviction. Yet even then, even in 1844, when he enlarged his notes into a written draft, he kept the secret to himself as far as the public were concerned, only confiding it to a few kindred spirits like Lyell and J. D. Hooker. And what was the secret? That the species had not been formed once and for all in one creative act or in a series of such acts; that they were not immutable, but had evolved by natural processes from a few simple primordial forms or from one. As we shall see directly, this was not the whole of the theory, but it was that part of it which Darwin then felt to be the most daring, and the most subversive of both scientific and theological orthodoxy. In that year, 1844, he wrote to his friend Hooker: 'At last gleams of light have come, and I am almost convinced (quite contrary to the opinion I started with) that species are not (it is like confessing a murder) immutable.' 'I think I have found out,' he goes on, 'the simple way by which species become exquisitely adapted to various ends.'[1] It is characteristic of Darwin's infinite caution and patience that even then he was fifteen years from the date of publication of the *Origin*; and he might have waited longer still had not A. R. Wallace, in 1858, hit upon the very same theory, and sent him from the Malay archipelago a memoir embodying his conclusions. Here was a frightful dilemma: Wallace must be given all credit for his independent discovery, yet Darwin had written it all down fourteen years ago and had had the idea earlier still; was all his toil and devotion to go for nothing, simply because he had been superhumanly careful not to rush to a hasty conclusion? Everyone knows the story of how the dilemma was resolved, and it does endless credit to both Wallace and Darwin. By the advice of Lyell and Hooker, who knew of Darwin's priority, papers by both men were communicated simultaneously to the Linnaean Society in 1858, and Darwin then proceeded to extract, from his huge accumulation of notes, the material for the *Origin*. Wallace always looked up to Darwin as his leader and master, and never (like some lesser men) grudged Darwin the lion's share of the glory; and Darwin, on his side, always treated Wallace, both privately and in print, as co-discoverer. All honour to such men, and to the Victorian age that produced them The cause of science —yes, and of agnosticism too—derived great strength at that time from the moral nobility of its champions.

Such then, was the man who was held by many to have abolished God, undermined the authority of scripture, degraded man to the level of the beasts that perish, and

[1] *Life and Letters of Charles Darwin* (1887), vol. II, p. 23.

abandoned the universe to the vagaries of blind chance. To understand how this could be, we must look carefully at the main argument of the book itself. I will first quote two passages, one from the Introduction, and the second from the last chapter:

(i) I can entertain no doubt, after the most deliberate study and dispassionate judgment of which I am capable, that the view which most naturalists until recently entertained, and which I formerly entertained —namely, that each species has been independently created—is erroneous. I am fully convinced that species are not immutable; but that those belonging to what are called the same genera are lineal descendants of some other and generally extinct species, in the same manner as the acknowledged varieties of any one species are the descendants of that species. Furthermore, I am convinced that Natural Selection has been the most important but not the exclusive, means of modification.[1]

(ii) I have now recapitulated the facts and considerations which have thoroughly convinced me that species have been modified, during a long course of descent. This has been effected chiefly through the natural selection of numerous successive, slight, favourable variations; aided in an important manner by the inherited effects of the use and disuse of parts; and in an unimportant manner . . . by the direct action of external conditions, and by variations which seem to us in our ignorance to arise spontaneously.[2]

Darwin begins, then, with the well-known tendency of all offspring, whether of plants or of animals, to vary, however slightly, from the parent stock. It is owing to

---

[1] *Origin of Species* (Popular Impression of the 6th ed., 1917), p. 4.
[2] *ibid.*, p. 395.

this tendency that man is able to breed various special strains of horses, sheep, dogs, pigeons, etc., or on the other hand of edible or ornamental plants. By keeping the minutest watch on variations, and by breeding in successive generations only from those varieties which show a tendency in the desired direction, man has produced for his own use or delight many kinds of animals or vegetables which differ enormously from the original stock. This is artificial selection, and its universally acknowledged success is the result of the adding up, by men, of the 'successive, slight, favourable variations' as and when they happen to appear, and the rejection of those that are unfavourable. Darwin tells us that on his return from the *Beagle* he began to collect every possible fact bearing upon the variation of creatures under domestication, not only reading every particle of relevant printed matter he could lay hands on, but consorting with stock-breeders and pigeon-fanciers to hear them talk and learn their methods. He soon saw (what indeed every breeder had known from time immemorial) that 'selection was the key-note of man's success in making useful races of animals and plants', but how selection could operate in Nature, assuming that no superhuman mind was at work there, remained as yet a mystery to him. Then as he tells us in the *Autobiography*, 'In October 1838 . . . I happened to read for amusement [an odd sort of diversion, one would think] Malthus on *Population* . . .' Now Darwin (like Wordsworth in this respect if in no other) owed much more to Nature than to books. He did not arrive at his results by reading the works of his precursors, but by studying Nature herself with that infinite capacity for taking pains, coupled with the power to make inspired guesses, which together constitute what we call 'genius'. But here, for once, it was a book which gave the final shake to the slowly forming crystal of his theory: the book with which Malthus alarmed the nineteenth century by showing that population tends to increase up to the limits of subsistence, and seemed likely, unless some check could be devised, to increase beyond them.

> ... being well prepared [Darwin goes on] to appreciate the struggle for existence which everywhere goes on from long-continued observation of the habits of animals and plants, it at once struck me that under these circumstances favourable variations would tend to be preserved, and unfavourable ones to be destroyed. The result of this would be the formation of new species. Here then, I had at last a theory by which to work....'[1]

Thus Darwin fitted the links into his chain of argument: the enormous fecundity of living creatures, the ensuing struggle for existence, and the survival of the fittest through natural selection. Selection designedly employed by man in the production of desired breeds goes on automatically in Nature through the elimination of creatures less fit to cope with the competitive *mêlée* and the preservation of the more fit, who survive to transmit their gifts and graces to their offspring.

'This', says Darwin (in the Introduction of the *Origin*), 'is the doctrine of Malthus applied to the whole animal and vegetable kingdoms.' The point was elaborated by J. Arthur Thomson in the Cambridge Centenary and Jubilee volume of fifty years ago (*Darwin and Modern*

---

[1] Lady Nora Barlow (editor), *The Autobiography of Charles Darwin* (1958), p. 120.

Science, 1909). He points out that Malthus also furnished
a clue to A. R. Wallace, and that Herbert Spencer, before
1859, had published an article on the theory of population, in which he had 'come within an ace of recognizing
that the struggle for existence was a factor in organic
evolution'. Thomson's comment is that Darwin, Wallace
and Spencer had all been 'led from a social problem to a
biological theory', and that to grasp this co-relation of
the biological theory with contemporary social problems is
more important than to ferret out 'anticipations' of the
theory in older scientific books which Darwin had mostly
not read. He further quotes an interesting passage from
the article 'Biology' in *Chambers's Encyclopaedia*, in which
the writer (P. Geddes) argues that the replacement of
Paley by Darwin, as chief interpreter of the order of
nature, is not just the replacement of anthropomorphism
by science, but of an eighteenth-century kind of anthropomorphism by a nineteenth-century kind. For

> the place vacated by Paley's theological and meta-
> physical explanation [says Geddes] has simply been
> occupied by that suggested to Darwin and Wallace by
> Malthus in terms of the prevalent severity of industrial
> competition, and those phenomena of the struggle for
> existence which the light of contemporary economic
> theory has enabled us to discern have thus come to
> be temporarily exalted into a complete explanation of
> organic progress.[1]

This shows what may happen when Darwin gets into the
clutches of a smart intellectual. We are apt to surrender
outright to such swift generalizations, and I am not deny-

[1] J. Arthur Thomson, 'Darwin's Predecessors'; chap. II in *Darwin and
Modern Science* (Cambridge 1909), p. 15.

ing that connexions can often be found between scientific, philosophical or even religious ideas and the social conditions in which they were conceived. No doubt it is not accidental that the century which produced the natural selection theory was also the century of *laissez-faire* economics. Yet how misleading is the suggestion that Darwin saw Nature in terms of 'the prevalent severity of industrial competition'! Though a benevolent man, he never bothered about 'the condition of England question'; his thoughts hovered over the Galapagos Islands, the forests of Brazil or the coast of Peru much more than over Manchester or Birmingham; and to imply that he first pondered the horrors of industrialism, and then applied his reflections to the animal and vegetable kingdoms, is as perverse as those Marxian analyses of poets and novelists which bored us so much about twenty-five years ago. One problem alone interested Darwin, namely, how species are formed, and Malthus meant nothing to him save for his fruitful hint on this. Moreover, as Thomson rightly adds, the *validity* of a scientific theory does not depend on what may have helped to suggest it. It may be safely said, on the other hand, that any debt of Darwin's to social theory was repaid with usury, for many sociologists and others afterwards tried to interpret human history on Darwinian lines, either approving or disapproving of *laissez-faire* according to the direction of their political and economic sympathies. Opinion was divided between those who thought that, to secure the best results, the struggle between individuals, classes and nations should go on, and those who held that man, whatever his ancestry, was now an ethical being, and must transcend or control the struggle in the interests of ideal ends.

But, grim as Darwin's picture of Nature's ruthlessness might be, it was not this that aroused so much bitter opposition. The picture might well, in spite of the optimism of a Paley or a Wordsworth, be true; and readers of Tennyson, for a decade before the *Origin* appeared, had been familiarized with the more dismal implications of evolutionary science. What caused most of the offence was the apparent banishment of the idea of God the creator and designer of the universe to such a distance that it lost all religious meaning; and the substitution of Chance for Purpose as the main explanatory principle. There was another, and in a sense an even graver, cause of offence: if all living beings were descended from a few primordial forms, or from one, then man too must be so descended. Darwin had deliberately refrained from emphasizing this inference in the *Origin*, lest the scandal of it should hamper the acceptance of his main doctrine. All he there says is that, by his own and Herbert Spencer's evolutionary theories, 'much light will be thrown on the origin of man and his history'.[1] But this hint was enough, and in any case the implication of man's pithecoid descent lay near the surface of the whole argument (to be brought out into the open later in *The Descent of Man*, 1871). It was immediately assumed by his opponents that Darwin had robbed man of his proud superiority, levelled him with the beasts, and abrogated, along with his divine origin, his spiritual status: his free will, his participation of the divine nature, and his hopes of heaven. Man had

[1] *Origin of Species*, ed. cit., p. 402.

lived for so long with the idea of God as Creator, and with the idea of Nature as evidence of his purpose and design, that they were shocked to hear that the creatures had 'just growed' instead of being made fully formed by the divine craftsman, and that the exquisite adaptations of organs to their environment were the result, not of design, but of the natural selection of random variations that happened to be favourable.

Darwin himself wondered, or affected to wonder, what all the fuss was about. The *Origin* itself contains very few explicit references to the controverted questions. Heretical though its tendency might be (and we must remember that 'mutability' was a scientific heresy at that time, as well as a theological one), it mostly skirts the metaphysical danger-zones at a discreet distance. And so far was Darwin from intending any frontal assault upon religion, that he went out of his way to disclaim such a notion. He said, in old age, that theistic belief or senti-ment was still strong in his mind about the time when he wrote the *Origin*, and this may partly explain his occasional use, in that book, of the words 'God' and 'Creator', and his attempt, near its conclusion, to recon-cile his theory with religion.

I see no reason [he there says] why the views given in this volume should shock the religious feelings of any one. It is satisfactory as showing how transient such impressions are, to remember that the greatest discovery ever made by man, namely, the law of the attraction of gravity, was also attacked by Leibnitz, as 'subversive of natural, and inferentially of revealed, re-ligion'. A celebrated author and divine [he goes on (it was Charles Kingsley)] has written to me that 'he has gradually learnt to see that it is just as noble a conception of the Deity to believe that He created a few original forms capable of self-development into other and needful forms, as to believe that He required a fresh act of creation to supply the voids caused by the action of His laws'.

... To my mind it accords better with what we know of the laws impressed upon matter by the Creator, that the production and extinction of the past and present inhabitants of the world should have been due to secondary causes, like those determining the birth and death of the individual. When I view all beings not as special creations, but as the lineal descendants of some few beings which lived long before the first bed of the Cambrian series was deposited, they seem to me to become ennobled.

And he ends the whole book with these words:

There is grandeur in this view of life, with its several powers, having been originally breathed by the Creator into a few forms or into one; and that ... from so simple a beginning endless forms most beautiful and most wonderful have been, and are being evolved.[1]

There might be grandeur in it for Kingsley, Aubrey Moore and a few other resolute liberals, but not for Samuel Wilberforce or Dr Pusey or the general mass of Christian believers and their ecclesiastical spokesmen. To them, in spite of Darwin's pious gesture of appeasement, it seemed that a Deity whose last recorded act was that of 'breathing life into a few forms or into one' must in so doing have breathed his last, or at least rested from his labours for ever after and not merely on the seventh day. Darwin's vestigial theism was no comfort to them; his

[1] *Origin of Species, ed. cit.*, pp. 396, 402-3.

substitution of chance for design seemed to place him in the atheistical succession from Epicurus and Lucretius and all the later materialists.

Although, as I have said, Darwin did not intend to attack the Bible, or the Church, or Christianity, he had one polemical aim which is in the forefront of the argument throughout, namely to expose the errors of other naturalists—whether, like Lamarck, his own grandfather Erasmus Darwin, or the author of *Vestiges of Creation* (Chambers), they were evolutionists on 'wrong' principles, or whether, like Linnaeus, Cuvier or Agassiz, they held the immutability and the 'special creation' of species. He argues repeatedly, explicitly, and with a wealth of illustration, against the view that species were supernaturally 'created', i.e. created by some inconceivable and unexplainable divine act either in the beginning or at many successive geological crises. Do the 'creationists' really believe, he asks (and in 1859 these included most of his *scientific* contemporaries), 'that at innumerable periods in the earth's history certain elemental atoms have been commanded suddenly to flash into living tissues? Were all the infinitely numerous kinds of animals created as eggs or seed, or as full grown? and in the case of mammals, were they created bearing the false marks of nourishment from the mother's womb?'[1] In later editions Darwin apologized for implying that his scientific contemporaries still believed such things; he has retained this and other passages of the *Origin* for their historical interest, and to illustrate what scientists believed before he had converted them. One of the main burdens of the argument

[1] *ibid.*, pp. 397-8.

throughout is that many facts, inexplicable by the theory
of special creation, become comprehensible on the theory
of natural selection: such facts, for example, as the geographical distribution of allied species, the repetition of
past history in the development of the embryo, and the
existence of 'rudimentary' or 'vestigial' organs—i.e.
organs no longer useful to the creature.

> On the view [he says] of each organism with all its
> separate parts having been specially created, how utterly
> inexplicable is it that organs bearing the plain stamp of
> inutility, such as the teeth in the embryonic calf [which
> never break through the gum], or the shrivelled wings
> under the soldered wing-covers of many beetles, should
> so frequently occur. Nature may be said to have taken
> pains to reveal her scheme of modification, by means of
> rudimentary organs, of embryological and homologous
> structures, but we are too blind to understand her
> meaning.[1]

The special creation theory, he exclaims with unwonted
warmth,

> makes the works of God a mere mockery and deception;
> I would almost as soon believe with the old and
> ignorant cosmologists, that fossil shells had never
> existed, but had been created in stone so as to mock the
> shells living on the sea-shore.[2]

Were cuckoos 'created' that their chicks might eject
the other nestlings? ants, to make slaves of other ants?
ichneumon flies, to lay their eggs in the bodies of cater-
pillars? Is it not 'more satisfactory' to regard these and
many other suchlike phenomena, not as 'designed', but
as minor by-products of a grand law tending to general

[1] *Origin of Species, ed. cit.*, p. 395.   [2] *ibid.*, p. 122.

advancement—i.e. the command 'multiply, vary, let the strongest live and the weakest die?'[1]

But what of all the manifestations of Design in Nature, to which divines and philosophers had for centuries pointed as evidence of the Wisdom of God? What of the exquisite adaptations of organs to their purpose, of which Darwin had read in Paley, at the time of his undergraduate innocence? What, for instance, of the contrivance by which our food is hurled across the windpipe, so that every act of swallowing, as though in an access of divine virtuosity or bravado, becomes a triumph over deadly risk? What, above all, of that marvellous and intricate structure, the Eye? Could that have been built up by the accumulation of 'chance' variations? Darwin freely admits the force of this objection; indeed, he could hardly reflect upon such things 'without being in some degree staggered', and he confessed to Asa Gray (in 1860) that 'the eye to this day gives me a cold shudder'. Yet Darwin will not surrender. Once admit the constant adding-up of favourable slight variations by natural selection, and all is possible. The eye, like all 'beautiful adaptations', was not 'designed'; it came about, in the struggle for existence, because variations (beginning, in this case, with extra sensitivity to light in some part of a primitive lump of jelly), 'if they be in any degree profitable to the individual of a species, will tend to the preservation of such individuals, and will generally be inherited by the offspring'. 'Nothing', says Darwin, with that candour in meeting objections which perhaps won more converts than any of his other devices of persuasion—'Nothing at first can

[1] *ibid.*, p. 219.

appear more difficult to believe',[1] and this sentiment was heartily echoed by his critics, theological and biological alike. If a man could believe that, it was felt, he could believe anything.

Samuel Butler, afterwards (as we shall see) Darwin's implacable foe, was only expressing a misgiving felt by many others (including Darwin himself) when he complained that Darwin's book had been misnamed, since the *origin* of species was precisely what had been left unexplained. What had to be accounted for was the origin of variation itself, and this Darwin had ascribed to 'chance'. 'Chance' is a word often used to mean quite different things, and is therefore a fruitful source of confused thinking. Darwin explained that in nature nothing happens 'by chance', but all according to the strict determination of physical law. 'Chance' does not mean 'no cause': it means 'cause unknown'; it is, he said a term which 'serves to acknowledge plainly our ignorance of the cause of each particular variation'. Yet he habitually spoke as if the useful variations, which Nature selects from the mass of useless ones, were (like the latter) thrown up at random. And if things happen like this, it was felt, even though some unknown physical law lies deeply hidden beneath the seeming causelessness—if they happen thus, they happen without the conscious design of an intelligent agent.

In concluding this lecture, let me try to describe Darwin's own attitude to the religious scare he had caused. The first thing that strikes one is that he appears as an unimplicated and detached onlooker, contemplating

[1] *Origin of Species, ed. cit.,* p. 379.

24

from afar, with innocent surprise and mild irritation, the wranglings of men cleverer than himself. He thought of himself as what in one sense he was: a country gentleman of ample means, retiring habits, poor health, an obsessive passion for natural history, and no head for metaphysics. To a man so obsessed (*possessed* would be a better word) by his chosen pursuits, and 'enjoying' such truly Victorian ill-health ('I *never* pass 24 hours without many hours of discomfort'), it seemed very tiresome and inconsiderate of his critics to insist upon cornering him with abstruse arguments for which he had no time and no aptitude. 'With respect to the theological view of the question,' he wrote to Asa Gray (May 22, 1860), 'this is always painful to me. I am bewildered. I had no intention to write atheistically.' And he said once to his friend the Vicar of Downe: 'I do not attack Moses, and I think Moses can take care of himself.' He tells us in his *Autobiography* that while on board the *Beagle* he was still 'quite orthodox', and was even 'heartily laughed at by several of the officers . . . for quoting the Bible as an unanswerable authority on some point of morality'. Later in life he was found, by some German phrenologists, to possess the 'bump of Reverence developed enough for ten Priests'. I have already mentioned his recollection that, when writing the *Origin*, the theistic explanation was still strongly present to his mind. Throughout his life he had moods in which it seemed difficult or impossible to conceive 'this immense and wonderful universe, including man with his capacity for looking far backwards and far into futurity, as the result of blind chance or necessity'; and at such times, as he says, 'I deserve to be called a

Theist'.[1] Yet, by his own admission also, these impressions gradually became weaker; disbelief 'crept over me at a very slow rate, but was at last complete. The rate was so slow that I felt no distress.' From his letters we can learn something of the way in which his mind was working. For instance, in the letter to Asa Gray already quoted, we see him nagged by the problem of chance-and-design:

> I own that I cannot see as plainly as others do, and as I should wish to do, evidence of design and beneficence on all sides of us. There seems to me too much misery in the world. I cannot persuade myself that a beneficent and omnipotent God would have designedly created the Ichneumonidae with the express intention of their feeding within the living bodies of Caterpillars, or that a cat should play with mice. Not believing this, I see no necessity in the belief that the eye was expressly designed. On the other hand, I cannot anyhow be contented to view this wonderful universe, and especially the nature of man, and to conclude that everything is the result of brute force. I am inclined to look at everything as resulting from designed laws, with the details, whether good or bad, left to the working out of what we may call chance. Not that this notion *at all* satisfies me. I feel most deeply that the whole subject is too profound for the human intellect . . . Let each man hope and believe what he can. Certainly I agree with you that my views are not at all necessarily atheistical.[2]

In 1873, in answer to a Dutch correspondent, he wrote:

> I may say that the impossiblity of conceiving that this grand and wondrous universe, with our conscious selves, arose through chance, seems to me the chief argument for the existence of God; but whether this is

[1] Lady Barlow, *op. cit.*, pp. 92-3.
[2] *Life and Letters*, vol. II, p. 312.

an argument of real value, I have never been able to decide . . . I am, also, induced to defer to a certain extent to the judgment of the many able men who have fully believed in God, but here again I see how poor an argument this is. *The safest conclusion seems to be that the whole subject is beyond the scope of man's intellect; but man can do his duty.*[1]

This is in close accord with the well-known utterance of a celebrated contemporary of Darwin's—also an Agnostic —George Eliot, on the theme of God, Immortality and Duty: 'how inconceivable the first, how unbelievable the second, and yet how peremptory and absolute the third.'

In 1879 he dictated the following reply to an earnest German student who had asked for a statement of his religious opinions:

> Mr Darwin . . . considers that the theory of Evolution is quite compatible with the belief in a God; but that you must remember that different persons have different definitions of what they mean by God.

When the German student, unsatisfied with this meagre allowance, wrote back asking for more, Darwin adopted the tactics which had served him so often and so well in evading unwanted committees, functions and invitations: he is old, he is out of health, he is preoccupied, and he cannot spare time to answer unanswerable questions.

> Science [he adds] has nothing to do with Christ, except in so far as the habit of scientific research makes a man cautious in admitting evidence. For myself, I do not believe that there ever has been any revelation. As for a future life, every man must judge for himself between conflicting vague probabilities.[2]

[1] *ibid.*, vol. I, pp. 306-7 (my italics).   [2] *ibid.*, p. 307.

In the same year (1879) he wrote to J. Fordyce:

> What my own views may be is a question of no consequence to anyone but myself.

This remark, so typical of Victorian individualism, is also very revealing of Darwin's mentality. He, the Newton of biology, the central and most important figure in nine-teenth-century science; he, the author of books which had convulsed the Church and shattered the simple faith of thousands, actually thought that he could keep his religious views to himself, that they had no bearing on his work, and that they mattered to nobody. In the same letter, he goes on:

> But, as you ask, I may state that my judgment often fluctuates . . . In my most extreme fluctuations I have never been an Atheist in the sense of denying God. I think that generally (and more and more as I grow older), but not always, that an Agnostic would be the more correct description of my state of mind.[1]

The Duke of Argyll has recorded some significant words spoken to him by Darwin in the last year of the latter's life (1882), during a talk about the wonderful contriv-ances in Nature. The Duke had remarked that it was 'impossible to look at these without seeing that they were the effect and expression of mind'. Darwin looked at him very hard, and then said, 'Well, that often comes over me with overwhelming force, but at other times—', and he shook his head vaguely and added, 'it seems to go away.'[2]

It went away, and with it went, as Darwin sorrowfully confessed in old age, his powers of responding to music, poetry and landscape, in all of which he had once de-

---

[1] *Life and Letters*, vol. I, p. 304.   [2] *ibid.*, p. 316 (footnote).

lighted. 'My mind', he said, 'seems to have become a kind of machine for grinding general laws out of large collections of facts.' Significantly enough, this is the very point seized upon by Pusey in a sermon preached in 1878 called 'Un-Science, Not Science, Adverse to Faith', and it will not be amiss for us to slip round for a moment to the theological side of the Iron Curtain and look at Darwin through the eyes of this subtle schoolman. The Tractarian leader had no difficulty in showing that Darwin's argument is incoherent when pressed back into that metaphysical hinterland which was Pusey's native country, but which Darwin regarded as the region of insoluble and boring puzzles. Pusey does not object to 'transformist' theories so long as they leave us God in the beginning; indeed, he claims that Evolution as such is perfectly in accord with the teaching of Western theology since Augustine (a point to which I shall return later). He grants that Darwin, however perfunctorily, has left us the Creator who originally breathed life into a few forms, or into one. Darwin then, he admits, is not an Atheist. He does not deny God, but he does something worse: he forgets Him. This is worse than denial, for denial at least implies the presence in the mind of the object denied, whereas it is of the essence of Darwinism to eliminate God, as far as may be, from our thoughts about the Creation and its history. Pusey connects this loss of spiritual perception—the common outcome of modern science, though not, he thinks, of the older science from Copernicus to Newton—with the narrowing effects of specialization. He quotes from Newman the remark that 'any one study . . ., exclusively pursued, deadens in the

mind the interest, nay the perception, of any other'—
an utterance strikingly confirmed by Darwin himself in
the confessions I have just quoted. According to Pusey,
Darwin's inconsistency as a theologian is that he first
brings in God to avoid the eternity of matter or spon-
taneous generation, and then eliminates Him 'from all
interference with the works which He has made'. We
know, from a letter written after reading Pusey's sermon
(to C. Ridley, November 28, 1878), that Darwin never
troubled himself about 'such insoluble questions' as the
'eternity of matter', and claimed to have written the
Origin without any relation whatever to Theology'.[1] He
probably never realized that the eternity of matter was
the only logical alternative to 'creation'. But this same
metaphysical unawareness led him also, almost without
noticing it, to replace the absent God with a latent personification of Nature, or even of 'Natural Selection'
itself. True, he catches himself out from time to time, and
warns us that he is only speaking metaphorically when he
talks of Natural Selection 'observing minutely', 'with
unerring tact discovering each improvement for further
perfecting', and so forth. But he returns so habitually to
that way of speaking, that we feel Pusey to be right in
accusing Darwin of having himself introduced, into the
theological vacuum he had created, a power acting according to design.

It is perhaps the very heart of the religious criticism of
Darwinian or other science that in attending exclusively
to the How, it loses interest in the Whence and the Why;
loses interest in them and deflects attention from them,

[1] *Life and Letters*, vol. III, pp. 235-6.

without necessarily denying that such questions may rightly be asked. Science, *qua* science, must inevitably do this; its very *raison d'être* is to replace the unknown by the known, the supernatural by the natural, fable by fact, and while engaged upon this task it must be provisionally atheistic or cease to be itself. It would be foolish to blame Darwin for not having been a profound metaphysician or theologian; the work he did accomplish was more than enough for the lifetimes of several ordinary men. But there were and are others for whom God is no optional hypothesis, to be occasionally used when other explanations fail, but the central, all-demanding Reality; and it was left to such people to reconcile Darwinism with their faith if they could. The later history of Christian apologetics has shown that the thing could be done. It was done by affirming that God has not rested after the seventh day, but has been immanent in nature throughout, so that (as Aubrey Moore put it) 'the facts of nature are the acts of God'. One may go further and say that Darwin has positively (though unwittingly) helped to restore buoyancy to religion by forcing it to abandon some of its more untenable defences. Though scriptural fundamentalism was undermined by historical and textual criticism far more than by any direct attack from natural science, Darwin contributed his share to the weakening of that bibliolatry which was the bane of popular Protestantism. And in so far as he reduced the prestige of the old argument from design, he was discrediting what had always been, in reality, a precarious line of defence. As Pascal had long ago said, Nature proves God only to those who already believe in Him on other grounds.

LECTURE II

Evolution before Darwin; Darwin through contemporary eyes

IN the last lecture I referred to Pusey's remark that the theory of Evolution, as such, was in harmony with the teaching of Western theology since Augustine. Today I propose first to take up this hint, and sketch the history of the evolutionary idea before Darwin; and after that, by an examination of some of the reviews of the *Origin*, to assess the state of opinion in Darwin's own time, and the nature of his impact upon it.

Samuel Butler used to complain that so many Darwinians (including Darwin himself?) spoke of Evolution as if it were Darwin's own invention, whereas Darwin's theory was merely that evolution had come about mainly by natural selection. By now it is generally realized, I assume, that Darwin's importance lay not in promulgating evolution itself, but in demonstrating, with unprecedented thoroughness and knowledge, how it worked, and making people believe in it. According to Butler, 'Buffon planted, Erasmus Darwin and Lamarck watered, but it was Mr Darwin who said "That fruit is ripe", and shook it into his lap'. This is misleading if it is taken, as Butler meant it to be taken, as an aspersion on Darwin's originality. Darwin, as I have said, did not reach his conclusions by reading the works of older biologists, but by brooding for years, with intense concentration lit up by flashes of insight, upon the masses of facts he had himself accumulated. Although he had read his grandfather's *Zoonomia* in

youth, he knew much less than many of his critics about
the previous history of evolutionary thought, and was
rather surprised when various 'anticipations' of his own
theory were pointed out to him. Butler (the *advocatus
diaboli* in this case) was nearer the mark when he wrote[1]

> Less than twenty years ago we never met with, or
> heard of, any one who accepted evolution . . ., unless it
> was that some one now and again said that there was a
> very dreadful book going about like a rampant lion,
> called 'Vestiges of Creation'. . . . Yet now, who disputes
> the main principles of evolution? . . . It is not he who
> first conceives an idea, but he who makes the people
> accept the main conclusion . . ., who has done the
> greatest work as regards the promulgation of an
> opinion. And this is what Mr Darwin has done for
> evolution.

T. H. Huxley, Darwin's 'general agent', 'bull-dog' and
knight-at-arms, in his chapter 'On the Reception of the
"Origin of Species" '[2] after saluting Darwin as the Newton
of biology, goes on to show that the influence of Darwinian ideas has spread far beyond that special field. 'The
oldest of all philosophies', says Huxley, in one of those
passages of confident rhetoric in which all conceivable
dissentients are swept aside like cobwebs—

> The oldest of all philosophies, that of Evolution,
> was bound hand and foot and cast into utter darkness
> during the millennium of theological scholasticism
> [Huxley's reading was far wider than Darwin's, but
> perhaps it did not include Augustine and Aquinas].
> But Darwin poured new life into the ancient frame;
> the bonds burst, and the revivified thought of ancient

[1] In *Life and Habit*, 1878; p. 276 in 1924 ed.
[2] *Life and Letters*, vol. II, chap. 5.

Greece has proved itself to be a more adequate expression of the universal order of things than any of the schemes which have been accepted by the credulity and welcomed by the superstition of seventy later generations of men. The emergence of the philosophy of Evolution [Huxley adds] in the attitude of claimant to the throne of the world of thought, is the most portentous event of the nineteenth century.

It is true enough that evolutionary ideas can be traced back to the pre-Socratic philosphers, and although it would be quite impossible in our allotted time to tell the story in any completeness or detail (even if I were competent to do it), I propose now to turn a spot-light on a few points along the immense panorama. We must, however, bear it steadily in mind all the while that in doing this we are not describing the evolution of Darwin's own theory; Darwin knew little of this piece of intellectual history, and only became acquainted with some parts of it after the *Origin* was written. The point rather is—and it has been borne out more than once in the history of ideas—that the Greeks, at one time or another, thought of almost every conceivable theory, and that whenever some defeat of Christian thinking has left a vacuum, what has rushed in to fill it has almost necessarily been a Greek idea.[1]

Although in Thales, Anaximander, Anaximenes and Xenophanes there are scattered suggestions of an evolutionary development of all things, including living creatures, out of water or primordial slime, and although Heraclitus offered the notion of a continuous flux of

[1] In much of what follows I am indebted to H. F. Osborn's *From the Greeks to Darwin* (New York 1894).

34

becoming, it is with Empedocles (495-435 B.C.) that we may best begin. Empedocles taught that the world was composed of four elements, continually tossed to and fro by the opposing forces of attraction (love) and repulsion (hate). From this chance play of love and hate Nature throws up all conceivable forms, including plants and animals: plants first, and then after long 'effort' and trial, animals. Many of these living forms are incomplete or monstrous, and only those are preserved which are fitted to survive.

Democritus and Anaxagoras between them gave us the two possible worlds that still (*mutatis mutandis*) confronted each other in Darwin and Paley: Democritus, the world of atoms and chance unordered by reason; and Anaxagoras one of intelligent design—though he appears not to have seen the origin of life as an instance of this.

On Aristotle (384-322 B.C.) I want to dwell a little longer, for, as might be expected of so great a thinker, he raises most of the relevant issues. It is especially interesting too, that Aristotle is the only ancient writer referred to by Darwin in the 'Historical Sketch' which he added to the third and succeeding editions of the *Origin*, and that he misunderstood the drift of the passage he quotes from the *Physics*. Aristotle was a teleologist, seeing Nature as a graded system ordered towards the perfection of each form from inorganic matter up to Man. Always the movement is from the less perfect to the more perfect, and movement is change towards the actualization of what is potential. Inorganic passes into organic by direct metamorphosis, life being generated from matter; and owing to the resistance of matter to form, Nature can only rise

by degrees from lower to higher types. Design and purpose are everywhere apparent in Nature, she belonging,
as he says, to 'the class of causes which act for the sake
of something'. Matter and force, regarded by some of the
earlier philosophers as sole causes, are in truth (as Jaeger
puts it)[1] only 'Nature's handymen; she herself is the
builder proceeding according to an inner plan and idea'.
As a thinker who believed that Nature is purposive,
striving always after the better, Aristotle makes a point
of refuting Empedocles and others who had taught that
chance rules supreme, and that the existing forms and
adaptations are simply those which survived because they
happened to be fitted for survival. He carefully considers
the Empedoclean notions, and he admits that some things
seem to happen in Nature by 'necessity', as when clouds
drop rain because they must, and not 'in order' to water
the crops; or by 'chance', as when the rain falls on a
farmer's threshing-floor, not *in order* to spoil his dry grain
but because it just happened so. Such things being so, it
has been possible to argue (he goes on) that the same is
true of the parts of animals. Our teeth, for instance, the
front ones sharp 'for' tearing, and the molars broad,
and 'useful for' grinding—these arose, they say, from
'necessity', and so with all the other parts in which we
suppose that there is a purpose. 'Wherever, then,' says
Aristotle, continuing his summary of his opponent's
view,

> all the parts came about just what they would have been
> if they had come to be for an end, such things survived,
> being organized spontaneously in a fitting way; whereas

[1] Werner Jaeger, *Aristotle* (Oxford 1934), p. 386.

those which grew otherwise perished, and continue to perish, as Empedocles says his man-faced ox-progeny did.

Such are the arguments (and others of the kind) which may cause difficulty on this point. Yet it is impossible that this should be the true view. For teeth and all the other natural things either invariably or normally come about in a given way; but of not one of the results of chance or spontaneity is this true. If then, it is agreed that things are either the result of coincidence or for an end, and these cannot be the result of coincidence or spontaneity, it follows that they must be for an end; and that such things are all due to nature even the champions of the Theory which is before us would agree. Therefore action for an end is present in things which come to be and are by nature.[1]

This is the passage referred to in Darwin's 'Historical Sketch', and I suspect that he only read, and read carelessly, that part of it which he quotes as having been pointed out to him. Anyone who will compare the quotation in the 'Historical Sketch' with the passage I have just extracted will see that Darwin stands Aristotle on his head, praising him faintly for foreshadowing the principle of natural selection, and not realizing that the phrases he quotes are part of the summary of the Empedoclean position, which Aristotle gives merely to demonstrate its absurdity. His quotation stops just at the point where Aristotle begins to state his own teleological view, which of course would have been unacceptable to Darwin.

In any complete account of this subject one would have to dwell next upon Epicurus and Lucretius, true

[1] Aristotle, *Physics*, book II, chap. 8 (198b), trans. by W. D. Ross.

predecessors of Darwin in that they were chiefly concerned to displace supernatural in favour of natural causation, and to exclude teleology in favour of the mechanical movements of atoms in the void. But I must pass on to enquire what warrant Pusey had for claiming that Evolution was in harmony with Christian teaching since Augustine. Both St Augustine and St Thomas Aquinas can be said to have held views about the Creation far more consonant with Darwin's than is often supposed, and far more 'enlightened' (if that is the right word) than those of the fundamentalist Victorians who flung up their hands and cried that if Darwin was right, Moses must be wrong. Augustine glossed the creation story in Genesis by saying, in effect, that in the first days God created the plants and animals *causaliter*, that is, by infusing into the earth the necessary energy or potency so that it could thereafter produce the creatures by natural unfolding, God resting (but only apparently resting) from his labours. St Thomas, expounding Augustine, sanctions this view as follows:

> As to the production of plants . . . some expositors say that, on this third day (of creation), plants were actually produced each in his kind—a view which is favoured by a superficial reading of the letter of Scripture. But Augustine says that the earth is then said to have brought forth grass and trees *causaliter*— i.e. it then received the power to produce them. This view he confirms by the authority of Scripture, which says, ' These are the generations of the heaven and of the earth, when they were created, in the day that the Lord God made the earth and the heavens, and every plant of the field before it was in the earth, and every herb of the field, before it grew.' Before, then, they came into

being on the earth they were made causally in the earth. And this is confirmed by reason. For in those first days God made creatures primarily or *causaliter*, and then rested from His work, and yet after that, by His superintendence of things created, He works even to this day in the work of propagation.[1]

Thus it was that Pusey, while denouncing Darwin for his theory of man's descent, and for the other reasons I mentioned above, could yet admit Evolution in the vegetable and animal Kingdoms as a perfectly orthodox doctrine. Aubrey Moore, one of the Victorian theologians who, after the first furore about Darwinism had simmered down, did most to promote the peaceful co-existence of Science and Religion, followed the same line, arguing that the antithesis between Creation and Evolution was unreal. 'The facts of Nature are the acts of God.' When we say 'God made us' we don't mean to deny the facts of reproduction; and similarly, we may say 'God made the species' without denying his method of evolving them. It was odd, Moore felt, that the question between the mutability or immutability of species should ever have appeared to be a religious question at all. Who invented the doctrine of immutability? Not Augustine nor Aquinas nor Bacon; the true culprits were Milton, Ray and Linnaeus—and especially Milton, whose description of the creatures emerging fully formed from 'the earth' had so captured his readers' imaginations as to be accepted as authoritative. Since we know that Milton was Darwin's favourite reading in his youth, and always accompanied

[1] The references are to Augustine, *De Genesi ad literam*, Lib. V, cap. V and XXIII; Aquinas, *Summa*, I pars, Qu. 69, art 2. Quoted by Aubrey Moore, *Science and the Faith* (1887), p. 178.

him on his excursions from the *Beagle*, let us briefly remind ourselves of the picture of Creation given in *Paradise Lost*:

[on the sixth day of creation God bids the earth bring forth beasts, each after his kind]

> The Earth obey'd, and straight
> Opening her fertile womb teem'd at a birth
> Innumerous living creatures, perfect forms,
> Limb'd and full grown. . . .
> The grassy clods now calv'd; now half appear'd
> The tawny lion, pawing to get free
> His hinder parts, then springs as broke from bonds,
> And rampant shakes his brinded mane; the ounce,
> The libbard, and the tiger, as the mole
> Rising, the crumbl'd earth above them threw
> In hillocks; the swift stag from under ground
> Bore up his branching head; scarce from his mould
> Behemoth biggest born of earth upheav'd
> His vastness; fleec't the flocks and bleating rose
> As plants; ambiguous between sea and land
> The river horse and scaly crocodile.
>
> Book VII, 453 ff.

It was this picture which Darwin spent the next twenty years of his life trying to blot out from his imagination. But if, as Moore remarks, neither the Bible, nor the Fathers, nor the Schoolmen require it, why should modern Christians feel obliged to defend what is now, in fact, an exploded *scientific* theory, and not a religious truth at all?

But I am anticipating. Evolutionary ideas were steadily gathering momentum from the Renaissance onwards. Bacon, for instance, speaks, in the *Novum Organum*, about the variations of creatures from their common forms, and the need to discover the cause of these deviations: 'for if nature be once seized in her variations, it will be easy to lead her by art to such deviation as she was at first led to by chance'. And he goes on to speak—unscientifically it is true, but suggestively all the same—of intermediate and transitional forms: e.g. moss is 'something between putrescence and a plant'; comets, between stars and meteors; flying fishes, between fishes and birds; bats between birds and quadrupeds.[1] Leibnitz taught that 'all natural orders of being present but a single chain'; and even ventured to add that the species might often be modified by great changes in habitat or environment.[2] The great philosopher Kant is to be found in a most interesting predicament in his reflections on this theme. He was caught between the mechanical and teleological world-views, and after attempting in an early work (*The General History of Nature and Theory of the Heavens*, 1755) to extend the domain of mechanism right through from the inorganic into the organic realms, he seems to have abandoned the hope that 'a Newton might arise even to make the production of a blade of grass comprehensible, according to natural laws ordained by no intention'. Such a Newton, as Haeckel says, afterwards appeared in Darwin.[3]

The great period of the *praeparatio darwinica* was the later eighteenth century and the earlier nineteenth, when the concepts of development, continuity, perfectibility and descent from a common prototype became the intellectual currency of a host of speculative philosophers and naturalists. Herder put forward the idea of a

[1] *Novum Organum*, Bk. II, xxix and xxx.
[2] Osborn, *op. cit.*, p. 96.   [3] *ibid.*, pp. 98 ff.

continuous transformation from lower to higher types; Schelling and Goethe maintained that all functions of life are the diverse modifications of a single force. Maupertuis, though derided as a pompous crank by Carlyle in his *Frederick*, threw out some remarkable hints, which would have pleased Samuel Butler (if he had known of them) a good deal more than Darwin:

> The elementary particles which form the embryo are each drawn from the corresponding structure in the parent, and conserve a sort of recollection (*souvenir*) of their previous form, so that in the offspring they will reflect and reproduce a resemblance to the parents [here Butler's Unconscious Memory theory is clearly anticipated, as we shall see in a later lecture]. If some of the particles happen to be missing, an imperfect being is formed . . . if the elements of a different species are united, a hybrid is produced. . . . In some cases a child resembles one of its ancestors more even than its parents; in this case we may suppose that the material particles conserve more strongly the habits they possessed in the ancestral form.[1]

The particles (and here Darwin would have agreed) do not always retain the parental order, but may fortuitously produce variations which accumulate and give rise to varieties and species; and the species are sterile *inter se*, so that new species are kept separate. Charles Bonnet, who is said to have invented the term 'Evolution', anticipated one of Darwin's main contentions when he proclaimed that there have been no separate acts of creation as in the Mosaic account, but that Nature has moved continuously by her own internal forces. However, he differed from

---

[1] *Système de la Nature* (1751), quoted *ibid.*, pp. 113 ff.

Darwin in believing that Nature contained an inner *perfecting* principle, and in teaching an evolution, not by modification and natural selection, but by the 'unfolding' of pre-existing 'germs'.[1] Meanwhile, among the pure naturalists, John Ray had stated the two criteria of species (permanence of form and appearance, and non-fertility with other species), and, most important of all, Linnaeus had added the authority of his great name to the doctrine that species are fixed units of direct creation, each one bearing the impress of the Creator's thought. It is remarkable that the naturalists, properly so called, should have been so much more conservative in their doctrine of species than the speculative philosophers; and it was owing to their prestige, above all that of Linnaeus, that Darwin at first found himself almost alone in affirming the mutability theory.

By far the most important of Darwin's precursors, however, were Buffon, Erasmus Darwin and Lamarck. The mention of these three names brings us back to Darwin's 'Historical Sketch', which jumps in a few lines from Aristotle to Buffon; but his treatment of them is perfunctory in the extreme, and it is clear that, apart from the above-mentioned reading of his grandfather's *Zoonomia* in early life, he was not deeply versed in them or conscious of any great debt to them. I know of no evidence that he had read Buffon or Lamarck in the original, or devoted much careful thought to them. In his *Autobiography* he tells us that while a student at Edinburgh he had listened 'in silent astonishment' to a panegyric on Lamarck by

[1] *Contemplation de la Nature* (1764); *Palingénésie Philosophique* (1768), quoted *ibid.*, pp. 119 ff.

Dr R. E. Grant, but 'without any effect on my mind'; and he adds that he had previously met with similar views in the *Zoonomia*, and that they too had produced no effect on him. He goes on to admit, however, that 'the hearing rather early in life such views maintained and praised may have favoured my upholding them under a different form in my *Origin of Species*.'[1] As Lady Barlow says in her recent edition of the *Autobiography*, the important words here are 'under a different form'; Darwin felt that he had supplied the necessary foundation of fact for what had hitherto, to some extent, been airy speculation. But Lamarck he consistently decried and almost certainly undervalued; in one of his letters he calls Lamarck's work 'a wretched book' (one wonders which of Lamarck's books he meant, and how much of it he had read), and says (in another) that he got 'not a fact or idea from it.'[2] Both these remarks, it is worth noting, are made in letters to Lyell, whose summary of Lamarck (in the *Principles of Geology*) Darwin had read, and who, somewhat to Darwin's surprise and annoyance, persisted in regarding the Darwinian Theory as a development of Lamarck's. Darwin hardly ever refers to Lamarck except in disparaging terms: 'Heaven forfend me from Lamarck nonsense of "a tendency to progression", "adaptations from the slow willing of animals", etc.!' (to Hooker, January 11, 1844); 'veritable rubbish' (to the same, 1844 n.d.); 'his absurd though clever work has done the subject harm' (to the same, 1849 n.d.), and so forth. Buffon he treats respect-

---

[1] *Autobiography*, ed. Lady Barlow (1958), p. 49.
[2] See Letters to Lyell, October 11, 1859, and March 12, 1863; *Life and Letters*, vol. II, p. 215, and III, p. 14.

fully, in the 'Historical Sketch', as the first to approach the theory of descent with modification in a scientific spirit, but complains that Buffon's opinions 'fluctuated greatly at different periods', and that he did not examine the causes or means of transformation.

We may safely say of Buffon, Erasmus Darwin and Lamarck that between them they had supplied nearly all the necessary ingredients, and that these ingredients only needed the added tincture from Malthus, the idea of natural selection and the massive substructure of Darwin's own observations, to produce the complete Darwinian dish. I do not propose to enlarge here much upon these precursors, because I think it will be more exciting to look at them later through the eyes of Samuel Butler. A few words will suffice at this stage.

Buffon (1707-88) taught the mutability of species under the direct influence of environment, the elimination of the unfit, and the preservation of the fit through heredity. He does not explicitly speak of the transmission of acquired characters, but this doctrine seems to be presupposed in his argument. Erasmus Darwin (1731-1802) traced back all life to a single 'filament' endowed with irritability and excitability, and shifted the emphasis from the Buffonian 'environment' to the Lamarckian (or rather, what later came to be so called) effort on the part of creatures to attain needed structures: 'all animals', he said, 'undergo transformations which are in part produced by their own exertions in response to pleasures and pains, and many of these acquired forms or propensities are transmitted to their posterity'. Lamarck (1744-1829) himself, who may or may not have borrowed from Erasmus Darwin, differed from Buffon and agreed with Erasmus in making environment act, not directly, but indirectly: thus, changed environment produces changed needs (*besoins*), these produce new habits, and new habits produce new or modified organs, which are passed on by heredity. Rudimentary organs are due to disuse. The inheritance of acquired characters was an essential postulate of Lamarck's argument, and the lack of evidence in favour of this principle, when understood simply and without elaborate qualification, has been one reason for the eclipse of his reputation. All three of these writers replace supernatural creation by natural causation, and all presuppose a common origin for man and the apes—though Buffon, with an irony that escaped Darwin's notice but not Samuel Butler's, affected to recant the heresy and submit to Revelation.

The eclipse of Lamarck is one of the most curious events in the history of science, for as to his brilliance there can be no doubt. But there was another, and a more important, reason for the contemptuous language used about him by Darwin; it was the idea, expressed in Darwin's phrase 'adaptations from the slow willing of animals', that Lamarck thought creatures produced new organs, or transformed old ones, by simply *wanting* hard enough and long enough. It is true that Lamarck ascribes evolutionary changes to a drive from within the creatures themselves in response to their circumstances, and not to mere natural selection operating upon chance variations; and that his teaching is thus fundamentally opposed to Darwin's. But, as Professor H. Graham Cannon has recently shown, Lamarck has been largely misunderstood because Lyell and others translated *besoins* as 'desires' instead of 'needs'. What Lamarck meant by *besoins* was, not consciously willed desires or aspirations, but subconscious needs. His second Law, as stated in the *Invertebrate Zoology* of 1815 reads:

> The production of a new organ in an animal body results from a new need (*besion*) which continues to make itself felt, and from a new movement that this need brings about and maintains.[1]

It may be that modern genetics and biochemistry will some day discover the mechanism behind the process thus metaphorically described by Lamarck; at any rate, an uneasy feeling has often recurred, in others besides Butler and Shaw, that Lamarck may have been in some sense right after all. Darwin himself had come round partially to the Lamarckian view (though without saying so) when, in later editions of the *Origin*, he inserted after 'natural selection' the words 'aided in an important manner by the inherited effects of the use and disuse of parts'. Darwin knew quite well that he could not explain the *origin* of variations, and it made him uncomfortable. It has not been explained to this day, though geneticists, I understand, have hopes of doing so eventually. For Darwin there was plenty left to do, even though he had to leave the cause of variation unexplained, and proceed from the fact of variation as a datum.

Let us now, in the time that remains, look at Darwin through the eyes of some of his contemporaries. In summarizing a small selection of the many reviews of the

---

[1] See Professor H. G. Cannon, 'What Lamarck Really Said' (in. *Proc. Linnaean Soc.*, January 1957); reprinted in the same writer's *Lamarck and Modern Genetics* (1959).

Origin I shall stress mainly the religious criticisms; it is, however, impossible to overlook the purely scientific objections, since it was by trying to represent his theories as scientifically unsound that many sought to blunt the edge of his alleged attack upon religion. This is true of Bishop Wilberforce's notorious review in the *Quarterly* (July 1860), with which we may well begin.

Wilberforce, after complimenting Darwin handsomely on his powers of observation and lively presentation, goes on to question the credibility of his theory of natural selection. There is indeed a struggle for existence, but there is no proof that favourable varieties 'accumulate' or that transmutations have ever actually taken place. With that ill-starred waggishness which led to his discomfiture at Huxley's hands (at the British Association meeting in Oxford, on June 30, 1860), the Bishop asks: 'is it credible that all favourable varieties of turnips are tending to become men, and yet that the closest microscopic observation has never detected the faintest tendency in the highest of the Algae to improve into the very lowest Zoophyte?' He seizes too, upon the imperfection of the geological record, on which Darwin had insisted so strongly. There are admittedly tremendous gaps, and many missing links, but how 'can we account for such distinct forms of life in the quietly succeeding formations except by distinct creations?' The new theory, he goes on with mounting animus, is based on 'the merest hypothesis, supported by the most unbounded assumptions'; it is the 'idle play of fancy, without [and here the worthy Bishop surely o'erleapt himself disastrously] the basis of fact or the discipline of observation'. 'Our readers will not have failed to notice', he complacently adds, 'that we have objected to the views with which we have been dealing solely on scientific grounds.' Facts of nature cannot contradict Revelation, for the God of Nature and the God of Revelation are the same. But errors such as Darwin's are not facts of Nature, and they must be condemned when they tend, as they do, to 'limit God's glory in creation, or to gainsay the revealed relations of that creation to Himself'. Man's place in Darwin's scheme is 'absolutely incompatible with the whole presentation of that moral and spiritual condition of man which is [Scripture's] proper subject-matter'. Darwin has offered as 'a degrading notion of the brute origin of him who was created in the image of God'. He may have tried to diffuse throughout creation the working and personality of the Creator, but this kind of pantheism is of no avail; 'however unconsciously to him who holds them, such views really tend inevitably to banish from the mind most of the peculiar attributes of the Almighty'.

From the Free Church side we have an article in the *North British Review* (May 1860), by a Reverend Mr Dunns. His argument is not dissimilar, though he also anticipates some of the points made by Pusey (see above, p. 29). Darwin's 'transformism' is a romance and a myth; there is no evidence against special creations and the immutability of species (no wonder Darwin sometimes feared that he was incapable of making people understand what he meant). Man can 'select' variations in domestic plants and animals, but it is incredible that 'Nature' should be able to do likewise, even if you personify her after banishing God from the scene. Darwin, indeed—

and here Mr Dunns makes a better point—has reverted to polytheism. In place of the one true God, he puts, first, the goddess Natural Selection, whose divine powers extend only to the selection, and not to the production, of the favourable variations. For these last, she is beholden to another Deity, called 'Chance'. And to explain 'exquisite adaptations' without referring them to God, Darwin deifies 'The Struggle for Life'. 'Mr Darwin's work is in direct antagonism to all the findings of natural theology . . .; and it does open violence to everything which the Creator Himself has told us in the Scriptures of truth, of the methods and results of His working.'

The Roman Catholic standpoint is represented by *The Rambler* (March 1860), which takes the high scholastic line, and while admitting that Mr Darwin is less deserving of the halter or the faggot than the grinning Voltaire, the whimsical Monboddo or the brutal Robinet, rebukes him severely for the mischief he has done. This reviewer, as is not surprising, brings into action the heavy artillery of Aristotle and the Fathers, and if Darwin's 'Historical Sketch' had existed at that stage, he could have exposed the error I mentioned above. The notion that living beings have been formed, not by creation for any final cause, but by the survival of accidental improvements —what is this but the Empedoclean teaching refuted ages ago by Aristotle? The idea of development from one primal organism is 'as integral a part of some heathen mythologies as is creation of Christianity'; and as for Darwin's assumption that all 'creationism' means irrational and arbitrary incursions of supernatural power, what said Augustine and St Basil and St Thomas Aquinas?

—that God had conferred upon the elements the powers which enabled them to evolve into living creatures. Evolution, then (it is Pusey's argument anticipated), is perfectly conformable with orthodox theology; what is heretical, is that teaching for which Aquinas censured Avicenna, that these powers were eternally inherent in matter *without* God. (Darwin, of course, had not taught this heresy, but I think this reviewer felt that logically he *ought* to have done so.) It is useless for Darwin's advocates, like the *The Times* reviewer (Huxley), to make out that Darwin must be met on scientific grounds alone. Such a theory as his, whether he intended it or not (we know that he did not), raises metaphysical issues, and his defenders must therefore not claim that, if the theory is physically plausible, 'we are not to be deterred from holding it by the trifling consideration of its incompatibility with any faith in the spirituality of the soul or the creative action of God'.

In another group of reviews, represented by the *Edinburgh Review* (April 1860, by Sir Richard Owen) and the *North American Review* (April 1860, by Professor Francis Bowen), we find dissatisfaction with Darwin's speculations on scientific rather than on religious grounds 'We have no sympathy whatever', says Sir Richard, 'with Biblical objectors to creation by law, or with the sacerdotal revilers of those who explain such laws.' And Bowen, after applying to Darwin what Pascal said of Descartes— 'it was his ambition . . . to do without God altogether, but he was obliged to suppose the Deity gave the world a fillip to set it in motion; after which there was nothing more for Him to do'— observes that he does not expect science to agree with Scripture; he is ready, he says, to 'call out with the loudest of the anti-Mosaic geologists, *Fiat scientia, ruat coelum*'. But both these writers, who class Darwin along with Lamarck and the author of *Vestiges*, find in him too much unverified hypothesis, too much 'proof' along the lines of 'it may be so for all we know to the contrary' (Pusey, too, in the Sermon already mentioned, complained that never had any system been built upon so many repetitions of phrases like 'perhaps', 'probably', 'possibly', 'it may be', 'it seems to be', 'most likely', 'it must be', 'it requires but a slight stretch of imagination to conceive that', etc., etc.). Both stress the inadequacy of Natural Selection to account for the extraordinary instincts of ants and bees, and for the existence in these of 'neuter' workers, which by definition cannot transmit their variations. Bowen makes excellent fun of the notion that bees, by natural selection, could have arrived at the mathematical precision (radius × 1.41421) of the distance of the centres of their adjacent wax spheres; and of the idea that the shape of their cells was reached by selection because of its maximum economy of wax— whereas bumble-bees, which are very slap-dash in this respect, have survived just the same. And where, he asks, are all the intermediate forms? We ought to have found in the rocks all sorts of forms representing Nature's boss-shots, 'gross, rude, and purposeless, the unmeaning creations of an unconscious cause, wholly out of line with such as succeeded in founding a permanent family'. He is sceptical about Darwin's claim that the geological record is incomplete, and about his plea for vast lapses of time. There is, he says, 'a very ancient, fish-like smell' about Darwin's 'ante-Silurian eternity'. It will not do to assume that the geological record is reliable when it speaks, but imperfect when it is silent. And it is notably silent, where it ought to be most eloquent, on the transitions leading up to Man (on this, as on other matters, I need hardly say, it has spoken unmistakably since those days). Another point made by Bowen, as also by Mivart and many others, concerns Darwin's assumption that *natura non facit saltum*; if a variation is to benefit the creature that manifests it, it must be, not slight and almost imperceptible, but 'of grave importance', a real jump in the right direction. How could there be anything but a jump, for instance, between vision and non-vision, air-breathing and water-breathing?

An attack came also from Darwin's friend and former Cambridge mentor, Adam Sedgwick, an eminent geologist who happened also to be a Christian. To Darwin himself he wrote a letter,[1] 'in a spirit of brotherly love', but admitting that he had read the *Origin* 'with more pain than pleasure'. What pained him most was Darwin's denial of final causes. 'There is' says Sedgwick,

> a moral or metaphysical part of nature as well as a physical. A man who denies this is deep in the mire of folly. 'Tis the crown and glory of organic science that it *does* through *final cause*, link material and moral. . . . You have ignored this link. . . . Were it possible . . . to break it, humanity, in my mind, would suffer a damage that might brutalize it, and sink the human race into a lower state of degradation than any into which it has fallen since its written records tell us of its history. Take the case of bee-cells. If your development produced the

[1] December 24 1859. *Life and Letters*, vol. II, pp. 247 ff.

successive modifications of the bee and its cells (which no mortal can prove), final cause would stand good as the directing cause under which successive generations have acted and gradually improved.

And in his *Spectator* review (March 24, 1860), Sedgwick wrote:

> . . . I cannot conclude without expressing my detestation of the theory, because of its unflinching materialism;—because it has deserted the inductive track, the only track that leads to physical truth;—because it utterly repudiates final causes, and thereby indicates a demoralised understanding on the part of its advocates.[1]

Against these and other charges Darwin was defended by Henry Fawcett (*Macmillan's Magazine*, December 1860) and Dr W. B. Carpenter (*National Review*, January 1860). Religious veneration, says Fawcett, will not be diminished by the discovery of the laws by which the Creator has, in fact, worked. Darwin has only done in his own field what Newton did in his: he has studied God's actual methods, instead of accepting the traditional fancies of pious ignorance. Carpenter, too, thinks that more honour is done to God by the development theory than by any doctrine of dramatic interventions, and echoes Baden Powell's disapproval of those who think we 'behold the Deity more clearly in the dark than in the light—in confusion, interruption, and catastrophe, *more* than in order, continuity, and progress'. The writer in *The Saturday Review* (December 24, 1860) realizes that 'Mr Darwin's views will cause painful anxiety to many who

[1] Quoted *Life and Letters*, vol. II, p. 298.

will regard them as hostile to the truths of Revelation',
but for his own part he has no such qualms. Sooner or
later however, Darwin will have to tackle the descent
of Man, and when he does, 'we should demur *in toto*' if he
tries to derive the immortal soul materially.

A few years after the triple explosions of 1859 to 1862,
a number of scientifically minded Christians, concerned
alike for science and for religion, got together and founded
'The Victoria Institute, or Philosophical Society of Great
Britain', which published its first volume of 'Transactions'
in 1867. Its President was the evangelical and philan-
thropic seventh Earl of Shaftesbury, and one of its Vice-
Presidents was P. H. Gosse, the father of Edmund Gosse.
The first of its seven declared 'Objects' was 'To investigate
fully and impartially the most important questions of
Philosophy and Science, but more especially those that
bear upon the great truths revealed in Holy Scripture,
with the view of defending these truths against the
oppositions of Science, falsely so called'. From this pros-
pectus and personnel it may be inferred that here we enter
the veritable Fundamentalist Underworld, and that the
shades of the prison-house are closing in upon us. The
inference would be justified; yet the more one studies the
history of thought the more one discovers that pure,
stark bigotry, for which there is nothing to be said, is
rarer than one supposed; and that for almost any intellectual position respectable grounds can be shown. It may
even happen, as J. S. Mill said, that in a minority group
fragments of truth may be preserved, which by the rest of
mankind have been ignored. A reading of the preliminary
essay in the Victoria Institute's first *Journal* partly

confirms this, although I am sure that the Institute regarded itself, not as a small heretical minority in Mill's sense, but as the defender and mouthpiece of orthodoxy and majority opinion. In this essay, by the Secretary, James Reddie, we find (leaving aside the writer's belief in scriptural inspiration) warnings which were too often ignored, and have had to be repeated again and again. The idea of the Institute, he says, is to keep a careful watch over scientific theories whenever they are confidently and dogmatically put forward as final truth, or as the whole of truth. We ought, he rightly says, to be always criticising scientific presuppositions and hypotheses; they are likely to be wrong, and are constantly being discredited in favour of others. Modern science has become too fragmented and departmentalized; the sense of the Whole has been lost. This is none the less true because the writer happened also to hold antiquated views about the Bible.

I have mentioned P. H. Gosse, who is known to many readers as the 'Father' in his son's book *Father and Son* (1907). Let me conclude with a few words about P. H. Gosse's book *Omphalos: An Attempt to untie the Geologic Knot* (1857), of which Sir Edmund gives some account, and which is certainly one of the strangest products of the fundamentalist controversy of a hundred years ago. As its date shows, it was not written in answer to the *Origin of Species*, but Gosse was a Fellow of the Royal Society, and knew from conversations there with Hooker and Darwin, what was in the wind. The object of his direct attack was Lyell's 'uniformitarian' geology, which had prepared the way for Darwin by showing that the earth's structure had been gradually formed, during unimaginable aeons, by the action of the natural forces which are still at work upon it now. Philip Henry Gosse, who was, in Huxley's phrase, 'an honest hodman of science', and who was also a strict believer in the 'plenary inspiration' of the Bible, suffered at this time agonies like those described by Bunyan, when two texts of an opposite tenour bolted into his mind simultaneously. Science said one thing, the Bible said another; science seemed right, but the Bible *could* not be wrong. After much thought and prayer, he hit upon a theory which, he felt, would untie the knot. With the self-confidence of fanaticism he wrote his book *Omphalos*, fully convinced that 'he alone possessed the secret of the enigma; he alone held the key which could smoothly open the lock of geological mystery'.[1] 'I have written it', he says in the Preface, 'in the constant prayer that the God of truth will deign so to use it [i.e. as providing the final reconciliation of Scripture and Geology]; and if He do, to Him be all the glory.' Chapter I gives a wide and surprisingly calm survey of the state of the question, and of the dilemma of the moment. Geology speaks everywhere of slow development and vast aeons; Genesis, of six days of creation. The Stone Book must speak truth, but so must God's written word: 'the records which seem legibly written on His created works do flatly contradict the statements which seem to be plainly expressed in His word'. Some (but not Philip Gosse himself) have denounced Geology itself as impious; others throw Scripture overboard; many, like Buckland, Sedgwick, Faber, Chalmers or Conybeare, have tried in vain

[1] *Father and Son* (Windmill Library ed., 1933), p. 109.

to reconcile the two accounts. Baden Powell thinks the Bible story 'only myth and poetry'; the author of *Vestiges*, 'coolly bowing aside God's authority', has hatched a scheme, by which 'the immediate ancestor of Adam was a Chimpanzee, and his remote ancestor a Maggot!'

Gosse's tone deepens as he prepares to disclose his secret: 'The true key', he writes, in solemn italics, '*the true key has not been applied to the wards*'. And what is the secret? That God's creative act was 'prochronic', that is, it created all things and beings instantaneously at a particular and arbitrary moment in their life-cycle; thus all the signs are found in them of previous phases of existence, which however never took place. Adam was created as an adult, yet he had an *omphalos* or navel just as if he had been born in the usual manner. The geological record shows truly what *would* have happened if God had chosen to fix the creative moment at an earlier point in the ideal history. The fossils represent God's conceptions of this history, but they never existed as real, living creatures. God might have decided to create the world in 1857; if he had done so, it would have been exactly what it is now (and Gosse describes the present state of things in lavish detail, to press home his point). Yet none of the apparent marks of past history would be real.

If madness, or a certain form of it, consists in accepting, and living with, a set of perfectly logical and consistent inferences from a totally unreal premiss, then *Omphalos* was a mad book. Poor Philip Gosse was dazed and broken-hearted when, after living 'in a fever of suspense, waiting for the tremendous issue' of his work, he found that 'atheists and Christians alike looked at it and laughed, and threw it away.'[1] The unkindest cut of all, he felt, was Charles Kingsley's letter saying that 'he could not give up the painful and slow conclusion of five and twenty years' study of geology, and believe that God has written on the rocks one enormous and superflous lie'.

[1] *Father and Son*, p. 109.

LECTURE III

Samuel Butler and Darwin

THE following words were written in the year 1921
(by whom, I will remind you afterwards):

> . . . as compared to the open-eyed intelligent wanting
> and trying of Lamarck, the Darwinian process may be
> described as a chapter of accidents. As such, it seems
> simple, because you do not at first realize all that it
> involves. But when its significance dawns on you, your
> heart sinks into a heap of sand within you. There is a
> hideous fatalism about it, a ghastly and damnable
> reduction of beauty and intelligence, of strength and
> purpose, of honor [sic] and aspiration, to such casually
> picturesque changes as an avalanche may make in a
> mountain landscape, or a railway accident in a human
> figure. To call this Natural Selection is blasphemy,
> possible to many for whom Nature is nothing but a
> casual aggregation of inert and dead matter, but eternally
> impossible to the spirits and souls of the righteous.
> If it be no blasphemy, but a truth of science, then the
> stars of heaven, the showers and dew, the winter and
> summer, the fire and heat, the mountains and hills,
> may no longer be called to exalt the Lord with us by
> praise: their work is to modify all things by blindly
> starving and murdering everything that is not lucky
> enough to survive in the universal struggle for hog-
> wash.

I do not know how many readers of today would recog-
nize this as Bernard Shaw, but it comes from the Preface
to *Back to Methuselah*. And Shaw goes on to remark that
'anyone who wants to know what it was to be a Lamarckian

during the last quarter of the nineteenth century has only to read Mr Festing Jones's memoir of Samuel Butler to learn how completely even a man of genius could isolate himself by antagonizing Darwin on the one hand and the Church on the other'.

Butler was indeed an isolated figure in his own life-time. He was also a *homo unius libri*; *Erewhon* (1872) was the only one of his many books on which he made any profit to speak of, and he only made £69, 3s. 10d. on that. On his other books he was out of pocket by many hundreds of pounds. And yet in 1906, four years after his death, Shaw saluted him as 'in his own department the greatest English writer of the latter half of the XIX century', and spoke of his 'extraordinarily fresh, free and future-piercing suggestions'. 'In Sicily', he adds, 'there is a Via Samuele Butler. When an English tourist sees it, he either asks "who the devil was Samuele Butler?" or wonders why the Sicilians should perpetuate the memory of the author of Hudibras.'[1]

Erewhon made whatever reputation Butler enjoyed in his lifetime as a man of letters. It was received (in Augustine Birrell's words) as 'a shrewd and biting satire on modern life and thought—the best of its kind since "Gulliver's Travels"', and it was taken about as seriously as such works usually are. Butler was set down as ingenious, amusing, original and quaint; he was perhaps rather unsound, but great fun all the same—especially as he could not possibly mean half he said. His subsequent works on religion and evolution were for the most part

[1] Preface to *Major Barbara* (1906; quoted from ed. of 1913, pp. 161-2).

ignored. He attributed this, as he says in a note of 1899, 'to the long course of practical boycott to which I have been subjected for so many years, or, if not boycott, of sneer, snarl and misrepresentation'. There is no doubt that he felt this keenly, even passionately; and yet he was some-times able to extract a kind of bitter sustenance from his own obscurity. 'I will willingly', he said 'pay the few hundreds of pounds which the neglect of my works costs me in order to be let alone and not plagued by the people who would come around me if I were known.' In a real sense he enjoyed what he called his 'Ishmaelitish position', and even hoped that the success of *Erewhon Revisited* (1901) would not tempt him to abandon the attitude which, to the satisfaction of his conscience, he had maintained so long. He could never have foreseen the posthumous success of *The Way of all Flesh* (1903), and still less the respect to be accorded to his evolutionary books in the first decades of the twentieth century. The fact is that Butler was an anti-Victorian about fifty years too soon, and came into his own at the time when the reaction against Victorian religion, Victorian home-life, Victorian morality and Victorian science was at its height—namely, just before and after the first world war.

It is not in the least surprising that Butler should have antagonized the Church; his revolt from Langar Rectory, and all that his father (the Rector) stood for, was the dominant *motif* of his life. But why should he have antagonized Darwin as well? It was precisely such refugees from orthodoxy who, for the most part, joined the Darwinian ranks most eagerly—'intoxicated', as Shaw said, 'with the idea that the world could make itself without design, purpose, skill, or intelligence'[1] and jumping at Darwinism as a glorious deliverance from Jehovah and Paley's watch. And, as we shall see, Butler did at first acclaim Darwin with exultation. How and why he changed his mind will be the main theme of this lecture.

Butler told J. B. Yeats, whom he met at Heatherley's art-school in the early years, that the *Origin of Species* had completely destroyed his belief in a personal God.[2] He had, however, already quarrelled with his father, refused to be ordained, thrown up his Cambridge prospects, and emigrated to New Zealand as a sheep-farmer before Darwin's book came out. On the very night of his embarkation at Gravesend, in September 1859, he had stopped saying his prayers and begun reading Gibbon. When the *Origin* came into his hands, soon after his arrival in New Zealand, it took him by storm. He became 'one of Mr Darwin's many enthusiastic admirers', and in 1862 he was writing to a friend that for the present he had renounced Christianity altogether. The first fruit of his enthusiasm was a contribution to the Christchurch (New Zealand) newspaper *The Press* (December 20, 1862): a philosophical dialogue ('the most offensive form', he afterwards wrote,[3] 'except poetry and books of travel into supposed unknown countries, that even literature can assume') entitled 'Darwin on the Origin of Species'. There is little in this except ardent advocacy and lucid

---

[1] Preface to *Back to Methuselah* (1921), p. xlvi.

[2] John Butler Yeats, *Essays Irish and American* (1918), 'Recollections of Samuel Butler'.

[3] *Unconscious Memory* (1880), p. 11 (1922 ed.).

exposition of the leading themes: fecundity, competition, natural selection. The imaginary antagonist is a man of straw who at intervals murmurs 'horrid', 'devilish', 'subversive of Christianity', etc. The most interesting statement Butler makes through his own mouthpiece is: 'I believe in Christianity, and I believe in Darwin . . . both being undoubtedly true . . ., the impossibility of reconciling them must be only apparent and temporary.'[1] It is difficult to be sure how to interpret this declaration. If it had come from the Butler of *The Fair Haven*, eleven years later, it might have been an ironic glance at the 'reconcilers' of contradictions in the Gospel narratives. Was Butler mature enough in 1862 to have meant this? It is more likely, I think, that the remark represents merely an attitude lightly assumed for purpose of this Dialogue. We know from his letter of this date that he believed himself to have rejected Christianity and taken up Darwin on the rebound. Later, his rejection of Darwin revealed that, though estranged from Creed and Church, he was on the side of religion against science—or rather against scientific pretensions. His deepest objection to Darwinism was never expressed as a Bishop would have phrased it; indeed, it was generally felt that such an infidel as Butler had no business to be attacking Darwin at all. But Butler's being was rooted and grounded in religion, and though he worshipped a strange God his complaint that Darwin had banished mind from the world placed him beside men who would certainly never have acknowledged him as an ally.

This Dialogue called forth a contemptuous rejoinder

[1] *A First Year in Canterbury Settlement*, etc. (ed. of 1914), p. 162.

(in *The Press* the following month, January 17, 1863) which Butler attributed to Bishop Abraham of Wellington. Though Butler replied to this in a strongly worded letter (March 14), it is possible that the Bishop had sown in his mind a mustard-seed which afterwards became a great tree. For the main point of his article (it was called 'Barrel-Organs) was that Darwin's theory was 'nothing new, but a *réchauffé* of the old story that his namesake, Dr Darwin, served up at the end of the last century . . . and Lord Monboddo had cooked in the beginning of the same century'. What proportions this idea afterwards assumed in Butler's mind we shall shortly see.

From this time onwards, for about twenty-five years, Butler was grappling with two great problems: the problem of religion and the problem of evolution. Merely to say this, however, conveys little; other men were doing the same. The point is that Butler, unlike most of his contemporaries, was committed to neither side, and so fell foul of the official exponents of both. At first, as we have just seen, he fled from religion to Darwin; but before long he was showing up Darwin too. Thus he never became a Huxleian agnostic, and never found in Darwinism a gospel to proclaim and a cause to champion. Similarly, although he could not do without religion, he could not do with orthodox Christianity. Butler was one of those unusual men who expect others to say what they mean and mean what they say. It is precisely men of this sort who write satire, because they are always finding their expectations disappointed; appearance and reality do not correspond as they should, and this discrepancy has to be pointed out. Feeling the need for religious faith, he expected to find the creed credible. He examined its evidences with meticulous care, and found it incredible. Hence his first extended work, *The Evidence for the Resurrection of Jesus Christ as contained in the Four Evangelists critically examined* (1865), which was afterwards partly incorporated in *The Fair Haven* (1873), and will be referred to in that context below. On the other hand, feeling the power and truth of the evolutionary idea, he expected to find in Darwin a clear and satisfying account of its mode of operation. He read Darwin as attentively as he read the Gospels, and found him not only incredible but also, as he believed—disingenuous. No wonder, then, that he antagonized both parties in the great Victorian controversy: he wanted Religion, but not the Creed; and he wanted Evolution, but not Darwin. The sense of having been taken in, bamboozled, was ever-present in his consciousness: he had been taken in by his father's bogus religion, and was he now to be taken in by Darwin's bogus version of evolution? And so for a quarter of a century he never ceased from mental fight on both these fronts; all his earlier books, *Erewhon* (1872), *The Fair Haven* (1873), *Life and Habit* (1877-8), *Evolution Old and New* (1879), *God the Known and God the Unknown* (1879), *Unconscious Memory* (1880) and *Luck, or Cunning?* (1886-7), were thrown off in the heat of it. And the fight continued to the end of his life, although his overt interests were switched in later years on to other topics: the origin and authorship of the *Odyssey*, the Life of his grandfather Dr Samuel Butler of Shrewsbury, the sculptures of Tabachetti, Shakespeare's sonnets. In all these activities too, however, except perhaps in the Life of Dr Butler, he appears as the unmasker of long-accepted error. Even in the *Life*, what aroused his excitement was the amazing discovery that such a man as his own father had had so admirable a father as Dr Butler. 'I have never', he once said, 'written on any subject unless I believed that the authorities on it were hopelessly wrong. If I thought them sound, why write? The consequence is that I have throughout, I am profoundly thankful to say, been in a very solitary Ishmaelitish position. . . .'[1]

Butler's next two articles show him busily at work playing variations on the Darwinian themes, though still unsure of his own direction. Of these articles (both of which afterwards appeared, worked up, in *Erewhon*) the first was 'Darwin among the Machines,'[2] and the second '*Lucubratio Ebria*'.[3] In these he is already wrestling with what was to be the central problem of his thought: the antithesis between mechanism and life. His mind was such that he could ask such questions as 'what *is* a machine?'; 'what does "being alive" mean?'; 'can "being alive" perhaps mean "being an exceedingly complicated machine"?'; and if so, in what sense is a machine not "alive"?' Darwin's account of evolution so completely eliminated the notions of mind and purpose that living organisms, in his scheme, become indistinguishable from machines. So Butler, though he had not yet explicitly defined this suspicion or recognized it as an objection, tried out the consequences of regarding machines as

---

[1] H. F. Jones, *Samuel Butler, A Memoir*, vol. II, p. 382.
[2] *The Press* (Christchurch, N.Z.), March 14, 1863.
[3] *Ibid.* July 28, 1865. Both are reprinted in *A First Year*, etc. (1914), and in *The Note-Books of S.B.* (1919).

animate, and as competitors with man in the struggle for existence. Machines are evolving so much more rapidly than man, that they will soon gain the upper hand over him; he will inevitably become their slave. Butler therefore recommends that 'war to the death should be instantly proclaimed against them. Every machine of every sort should be destroyed by the well-wisher of his species'.

This article was afterwards enlarged, and finally appeared in *Erewhon* as Chapters XXIII and XXIV ('The Book of the Machines'), where it figures as the work which, five hundred years earlier, had induced the Erewhonians to destroy all their machinery. In all this, we may ask, what was Butler really getting at? It is easy to misunderstand his drift, as indeed his contemporaries constantly found. I suggest that it would be a mistake to think that Butler was denouncing machines in the spirit of a twentieth-century humanist who shudders at the mechanization of modern life and the possible destruction of man by his own inventions. He was merely playing an intellectual game; trying how high he could build a card-castle of ideas before it toppled over. Or, to use a more appropriate metaphor (for after all Butler was a musician, amongst other things), let us say that he was taking a given tune and working out its possible development to the full. But the ideas themselves had no more relation to actual things than musical notes or algebraic symbols have. Butler himself made this quite clear, both in the Preface to the second edition of *Erewhon* and in a letter written to Darwin while the two men were still on friendly terms. In the letter (May 11, 1872) he tells Darwin that he is 'sincerely sorry that some of the critics should have thought that I was laughing at your theory, a thing which I never meant to do, and should be shocked at having done'. In the chapter on Machines, he continues, 'I have developed and worked out the obviously absurd theory that they are about to supplant the human race and be developed into a higher kind of life. When I first got hold of the idea, I developed it for mere fun and because it amused me and I thought would amuse others, but without a particle of serious meaning; but I developed it and introduced it into *Erewhon* with the intention of implying: "See how easy it is to be plausible, and what absurd propositions can be defended with a little ingenuity and distortion and departure from strictly scientific methods. . . ." ' In the same spirit he next proceeded to stand on his head and view the theory upside down: 'I soon felt that though there was plenty of amusement to be got out of this line [i.e. treating machines as animals], it was one that I should have to leave sooner or later; I therefore left it at once for the view that machines were limbs which we had made, and carried outside our bodies instead of incorporating them with ourselves.'[1] This is the theme of the second New Zealand article, called '*Lucubratio Ebria*', in which a good deal of the authentic Butler begins to appear—perhaps because, as he says, he 'believed more in the views it put forward'. Here the idea is that machines are the way in which the human organism becomes more highly developed. The Australian savage has no extra-corporeal limbs except a rug and a javelin; the nineteenth-century Englishman supplements his physique with organs such as an umbrella, a watch, a

[1] *Unconscious Memory* (1922 ed.), p. 15.

penknife; and, 'if he be a really well-developed specimen of the race, he will be furnished with a large box upon wheels, two horses, and a coachman'. By a natural transition Butler goes on to declare for the first time his admiration—so often expressed afterwards—for money and rich men. We all pay respect to wealth, and there is nothing in this to be ashamed of; it simply means that we are acknowledging a higher degree of evolution. 'He who can tack a portion of one of the P. & O. boats on to his identity is a much more highly organized being than one who cannot'; 'the Rothschilds are the most astonishing organisms that the world has ever yet seen'. In *Erewhon* this argument appears as an addendum of a few pages to the 'Book of the Machines' purporting to summarize the only serious Erewhonian attempt to refute the anti-machinists. Here he carries the line of thought one step further: 'that old philosophic enemy, matter, the inherently and essentially evil, still hangs about the neck of the poor and strangles him, but to the rich, matter is immaterial; the elaborate organization of his extra-corporeal system has freed his soul'.

The next round in the game of ideas was to try out one more paradox: machines had been treated as animate, and then as limbs; it remained to look upon limbs as machines, i.e. as things we had made of set purpose. 'A leg', he had said in *Erewhon*, 'is only a much better wooden leg than any one can manufacture.' And at this point the game refused to be a game any longer, and turned into something very earnest indeed. The new paradox took possession of him, and for several years he brooded, with a mounting sense of discovery, upon the mystery of how we, how all living creatures, came to be equipped with the organs, capacities, habits and instincts they possess. This new thinking resulted in the first of his serious evolutionary books, *Life and Habit*. It proceeded somewhat as follows. First, he asked himself how, if we made the superior wooden legs ourselves, we came to make them. Clearly it was not done consciously. How then—unconsciously? But how can we do things unconsciously? By habit. We acquire habits, such as reading, piano-playing or cycling, by conscious effort in the first place; but practice makes perfect, and the more perfectly we have acquired any technique the more unconsciously we perform its actions. The actions we perform most perfectly of all, such as digesting, breathing, circulating the blood, etc., are those of which we are least conscious. How, then, did we acquire these unconscious habits, which we have never consciously practised? In our ancestors, our past selves. Are we then indistinguishable from these past selves? Are we in some sense 'identical' with them? What *is* 'sameness' or 'identity'? Am I the 'same' person as I was yesterday, last year, fifty years ago, as a baby? Common sense answers yes, though not a particle of my material frame has remained identical throughout. But we cannot hold the common-sense view of personal identity without going back beyond the baby to the embryo, the germ-cell, the parents, and so on back for ever. 'Birth', he says, 'has been made too much of.' And: 'it has, I believe, been often remarked [meaning that it hasn't] that a hen is only an egg's way of making another egg'. 'We remember our past existences, though too utterly to be capable of introspection in the matter.' This unconscious memory is the clue to heredity; any offspring resembles its parents because it remembers best what it has been doing most recently. Instinct is inherited memory, memory of actions done repeatedly in innumerable past generations.

Butler had reached this point in his argument—had indeed, as he believed, finished his book—without thinking that he had deviated implicitly from orthodox Darwinianism; on the contrary, he hoped his work would be welcomed by Darwin as a footnote or adjunct to his theory. Then something happened which changed the whole current of his thoughts: he read St George Mivart's book *The Genesis of Species* (1871). This book, written by a Roman Catholic who was also an eminent biologist, was what first revealed to Butler the real direction of his own thought. Mivart, while believing in evolution, had suggested that Natural Selection could never account for the whole of it, and Butler at once felt that he had been humbugged again, this time by Darwin. He was amazed to find that a man could attack Darwin without attacking evolution itself, for hitherto he had assumed that they were much the same thing. He hastily re-read the *Origin of Species*, and found to his horror that according to Darwin the notion of instinct as inherited habit was a long-exploded error of Lamarck's. This sent him back to Lamarck, whom he found that he greatly preferred to Darwin. The final chapters of *Life and Habit* were hurriedly added in the excitement of his discovery that, though he had not known it, the spirit of his book had all along been teleological, and therefore hostile to any theory attributing evolution to the agency of Natural Selection working upon chance variations. What causes the variations themselves? 'To me it seems', he wrote, 'that the "Origin of Variation", whatever it is, is the only true "Origin of Species", and that this must, as Lamarck insisted, be looked for in the needs and experiences of the creatures varying.' 'One cannot look . . . for the origin of species in that part of the course of nature which settles the preservation or extinction of variations which have already arisen from some unknown cause, but one must look for it in the causes that have led to variation at all.' Lamarck had found the cause in the effort of creatures, in response to environment, to supply felt needs, and to develop new organs and habits accordingly. Darwin had allowed for no such effort, and had further given the impression of thinking (though doubtless he would have disclaimed this) that natural selection not only preserves the good variations but also accounts for them. If the Lamarckian sense of need, and the Lamarckian effort, are denied, what really distinguishes living organisms from machines? But if anything but chance causes the variations, what cause more likely than 'sense of need', or what Butler calls 'faith and desire, aided by intelligence'? Darwin himself, by including 'use and disuse' among the causes of evolution, had given his own case away without admitting or even appearing to realize it.[1]

Butler still respected Darwin for having done more than anyone else to make his generation believe in evolution, but he now felt that Darwin had deliberately blinded his readers to the true origin of variations. He wrote to his friend, Darwin's son Francis, regretting that his book had grown into a downright attack on Darwin's

[1] On all this, see *Life and Habit*, chaps. XII and XIII.

view and a defence of Lamarck's. But Mivart had opened his eyes to the need for something to account for and give an aim to the variations, and he now believed that for this purpose natural selection was 'a rope of sand'. And he saw that he was returning to Paley's position, except (and it is a big exception) that he wanted the design to come from within, and not from an external divine designer. 'Butler's whole nature', Festing Jones truly remarks, 'revolted against the idea that the universe was without intelligence . . . But where was the architect of the universe? He could not return to the Jewish and Christian idea of God designing his creatures from outside; he saw, however, no reason why the intelligence should not be inside'—so he incorporated God within the creatures as the life force.[1]

It is no part of my present purpose to describe in any detail the personal quarrel which soon afterwards arose between Butler and Darwin—or let us rather say (for Darwin was incapable of quarrelling) the personal misunderstanding whereby Butler came to regard Darwin as one of the Seven Humbugs of Christendom. This has already been done by H. Festing Jones, and (definitively) by Lady Barlow in her recent edition of Darwin's *Autobiography*. I shall only touch upon it because, as Butler himself truly said, 'the battle is one of greater importance than appears at first sight. It is a battle between teleology and non-teleology.'[2] Immediately after writing *Life and Habit* Butler read the 'Historical Sketch' (referred to above, pp. 35 ff.) which Darwin appended to

---

[1] *Memoir*, vol. I, p. 300.
[2] *Unconscious Memory* (1922 ed.), p, 185.

the third edition of the *Origin*. This led him to read most of the predecessors there mentioned, and in particular Buffon, Lamarck and Erasmus Darwin. One cannot doubt that he read them much more thoroughly, and with much greater critical acumen, than Darwin himself had ever done. Butler, remembering that the *Origin* had left him with the impression that Evolution and Natural Selection were almost the same thing, and that that thing was Darwin's own invention, was astonished at the completeness of the anticipations he found in these older writers. Why had Darwin not acknowledged his debts more fully, and why had he waited until 6000 copies of his book had been sold before acknowledging them at all? Could it be—and once the acid of suspicion had touched him it ate deeper and deeper into his soul—could it be that Darwin had deliberately played down the work of his forerunners in order to exalt his own? Had he not done this largely by speaking constantly of 'my' theory, by implying that natural selection was the sole explanation of evolution, that the two processes were virtually identical, and that he had discovered them both? Was it possible that Darwin, to whom Butler had owed his intellectual emancipation, was himself a fraud—and a worse one even than Theobald Pontifex? For what other reason than to advertise his own mindless, purposeless scheme could he have so depreciated the work of these forerunners, in whom the whole evolutionary theory is not only already full-formed but properly teleological as well?

In this frame of mind Butler wrote *Evolution Old and New* (1879), of which a large part consists in an account of the lives and works of Buffon, Dr Erasmus Darwin and Lamarck. He wrote it chiefly to refute the prevailing notion, produced by the *Origin of Species*, that if you accept Evolution you must reject all 'purposiveness'. He was afraid that the discrediting of Darwin, which he foresaw as inevitable, might endanger the continued acceptance of Evolution itself; but he believed that this could be avoided by removing the theory from its present pedestal and replacing it upon that erected by the older men. Let us glance at a few examples of his advocacy of these writers.

Darwin had accused Buffon of 'fluctuations' in his views; Butler, with his far finer literary perceptiveness, detected the irony behind these alleged shifts. Buffon, after throwing out the notion of the common descent of all creatures from one primordial form or forms, suddenly remembers that he is a Frenchman living under the *ancien régime*, and accordingly—after the manner of his kind—makes an ironic and purely routine genuflexion towards orthodoxy. His real though masked intention, Butler argues, was to convey the impression that man and the apes were descendants of a common ancestor. Buffon attributed modification to the direct influence of climate, food, changed environment and the like, whereas Erasmus Darwin attributed it only indirectly to these and directly to changed desires and the ensuing change of habits. What hindered acceptance of the Buffon-Erasmus Darwin system was the success of Paley's *Natural Theology*: 'The unfortunate failure to see that evolution involves design and purpose as necessarily and far more intelligibly than the theological view of creation, has retarded our perception

of many important facts for three quarters of a century.'[1]
Butler quotes from the *Zoonomia* of Erasmus Darwin, with
high approval, such things as his description of offspring
as 'a branch or elongation of the parent'; and his argument
that modifications in living creatures are in part produced by their own exertions 'in consequence of their
desires and aversions', many of these 'acquired forms or
propensities' being 'transmitted to their posterity'.
Lamarck he sees as a follower of Erasmus Darwin, and
possibly directly influenced by him. He quotes Lamarck's
eloquent defence of evolution as opposed to special
creation—a defence which renders superfluous all that
Charles Darwin has said on this topic. New surroundings
(*circonstances*), in Lamarck's scheme, give rise to new wants
(*besoins*), these to new habits and new organs; 'new
parts . . . become insensibly evolved in the creature by
its own efforts from within'. Our modern evolutionists
should in like manner admit 'that animals are modified
not because they subsequently survive, but because they
have done this or that which has led to their modification, and hence to their surviving'.[2] Herbert Spencer in
1852 stated the case for evolution perfectly; these were
the days, says Butler, 'before "Natural Selection" had
been discharged into the waters of the evolutionary controversy, like the secretion of a cuttle-fish . . . Volumes
may be written to adduce the details which warrant us
in accepting it, and to explain the causes which have
brought it about, but I fail to see how anything essential
can be added to the theory itself, which is here so well

---

[1] *Evolution Old and New*, pp. 195-6.
[2] *ibid.*, p. 302.

supported by Mr Spencer, and which is exactly as Lamarck left it.' Tyndall has spoken as if evolution itself were 'Darwin's theory', whereas Darwin's theory was merely that evolution came about chiefly by natural selection. But there is more to be said for evolution than that, and the idea that evolution is Darwin's theory will pass muster only with those who know nothing of its literature.

Though there is plenty of animus in this book, there is not yet the bitter resentment, arising from a sense of personal wrong, which runs through Butler's next work, *Unconscious Memory* (1880). I will not rehearse the details of this tiresome and unnecessary misunderstanding, but it is needful just to say, first, that Butler thought his own vindication of Erasmus Darwin had awakened Charles to the propriety of doing tardy justice to his own grandfather—of whom in the 'Historical Sketch' he had remarked, 'in the middle of a note in the smallest possible type', that it was curious how far Erasmus had anticipated the erroneous opinions of Lamarck. It was very right and proper that Charles should publish, as he did in November 1879, his book *Erasmus Darwin*. But this book, though it began with a long prefatory memoir by Charles, was in itself a translation from the German of an article by Dr Krause which had originally (February 1879) appeared in a learned journal called *Kosmos*. Darwin gave no indication that the translation differed in any way from the original article, though he mentioned in a footnote that Butler's *Evolution, Old and New* had appeared since Krause's article in *Kosmos*. Butler, reading the translation, was transfixed to find passages which could not, he felt, have been written except with reference to his own book. Above all he noted this:

> Erasmus Darwin's system was in itself a most significant first step in the path of knowledge which his grandson has opened up for us, but to wish to revive it at the present day, as has actually been seriously attempted, shows a weakness of thought and a mental anachronism which no one can envy.

' "That's me", said I to myself promptly.' With equal promptitude, Butler taught himself enough German to be able, within a fortnight, to compare the *Kosmos* article with the translation. As he had expected, he found in the latter many interpolations; and among them was the passage just quoted, which seemed to condemn him by anticipation. Yet Darwin had certified the accuracy of the translation. Here at last was plain confirmation of Butler's darkest suspicions; Darwin, recently saluted by Huxley, Ray Lankester and the rest as the greatest of living men, was an impostor, a humbug and a whited sepulchre. Butler hurled thunderbolts at Darwin in the press, and in private letters to the culprit himself. He got no proper reply. Darwin—dreamy, forgetful and withdrawn—was terrified by this clever and unpleasant Mr Butler, and rather than get involved in a distracting dispute let himself be persuaded by Huxley to ignore the enemy instead of giving him, as he could perfectly well have done, the simple explanation (that he had forgotten to restore an excised note stating that the Krause article had been revised and enlarged). But enough of this. For us now, the only remaining significance of the whole imbroglio is that it confirmed Butler in his opinion that

Darwin was a man of straw whose views were only correct when stolen from his elders and betters, and baseless when original. If Darwin could treat him, Butler, so dishonestly, no wonder he had treated his forerunners with similar disingenuousness.

From this time onwards Butler felt himself to be a confirmed malcontent, in sworn opposition to, and deliberately ignored or snubbed by, all Establishments whether ecclesiastical or scientific. Of the two main Establishments he actually preferred the Church. This may seem odd when one thinks of *The Fair Haven* and *The Way of All Flesh*; it becomes less strange, however, when one remembers where his affinities really lay. This Coriolanus, fleeing in dudgeon from his native city, had found the Volscians worse company than the Romans. He admitted freely that he knew nothing about 'science', but he knew that he possessed—what the professional scientists generally, and Darwin in particular, lacked— a clear brain capable of probing into the philosophical foundations of science. The professionals brushed him aside as an ignoramus; he retorted, quite justly, with the charge of superficiality. What did it matter that Darwin had spent a lifetime collecting facts if the theory he built upon them was incoherent or pernicious? The mindless theory of evolution chimed in exactly with the materialistic mood of the '70's and '80's, and Butler feared that the superstition of the Church would be replaced by a worse and more tyrannical superstition—that of science. The Church, with all its faults, had at least stood for 'grace of some sort', and had witnessed to the reality of the unseen. Science saw God nowhere; Butler saw Him everywhere—even in every atom of the universe, to which he came finally to attribute life. In *Luck, or Cunning?* (1887), his last evolutionary book, he remarks that there is no real antagonism between religion and science: 'religion is the quintessence of science, and science the raw material of religion; when people talk about reconciling religion and science they do not mean what they say; they mean reconciling the statements made by one set of professional men with those made by another set. . . .'[1] Religion, he wrote to Mivart (February 27, 1884), cannot be kept out of evolution:

> I see the action of God throughout the universe. . . . I imagine you to see God as something apart from the universe which he has taken and moulded, as it were, in the hollow of his hand, and into which he has breathed the breath of life. I see him as animating the universe— he in us, and we in him; so that the union between God and his creatures seems closer, more indissoluble, and, at the same time, more literal and bona fide than I can imagine it as seen from any other standpoint; . . . admitting design, as I cordially do, is it such a very great matter, after all, whether the designer is within the organism or without it? Surely this is a detail in comparison with getting people to see that there is design at all.[2]

'It is not the bishops and archbishops I am afraid of', he wrote to his sister.[3] 'Men like Huxley and Tyndall are my natural enemies, and I am always glad when I find church people recognising that the differences between them and me are, as I believe myself, more of words than

[1] *Luck, or Cunning?* (1922 ed.), p. 221.
[2] *Memoir*, vol. I, p. 407.
[3] March 29, 1883. *Memoir*, vol. I, p. 385.

of things.' In the same spirit he had written to Harvey Goodwin, Bishop of Carlisle (November 18, 1880), to whom he had sent a copy of *Unconscious Memory*. He hoped, he said, that his purposive theory of evolution might help to reconcile 'the two main opposing currents of English thought'—the one which starts from God, and the other which starts from the creation; both can meet in accepting an all-pervading mind and purpose, though they reach this conception from opposite sides. Miss Savage's comment on this need not shake our faith in Butler's sincerity: 'By all means make friends of the Mammon of Righteousness, and if you exploit that dear bishop I am sure you will do it kindly.' Such persiflage was necessary to the Butler-Savage relationship; it maintained the correct tone of naughtiness. But Butler meant what he said; though himself incapable of orthodoxy, he was aware of, and approved, the pro-religious trend his work might have for others. In *Evolution Old and New*[1] he had acknowledged the truth of Mivart's conclusion, that 'the material universe is always and everywhere sustained and directed by an infinite cause, for which to us the word mind is the least inadequate and misleading symbol'. He had even, in Appendix II of the same work, gone so far as to say: 'If the Church of Rome would only develop some doctrine or, I know not how, provide some means by which men like myself, who cannot pretend to believe in the miraculous element of Christianity, could yet join her as a conservative stronghold, I for one should do so.' Protestantism, he felt, had no future. Rome was the only possible nucleus of a future Church. The Papal infallibility,

[1] p. 399.

he conjectured, might give Rome the flexibility necessary to adapt it to the modern world. To fit this Romanizing pose into one's general notion of Butler one need only remember two things: first, that he always respected people who really believed what they professed to believe —as Roman Catholics did and Anglicans too often did not, and secondly, that Butler had a strong, imaginative sympathy with the Italian people, their beauty and their amiability, their art, their sanctuaries and shrines. As I mentioned earlier, it is in Sicily alone that there is a *Via Samuele Butler*.

There have always been a few who have thought, or hoped, that Lamarck and Butler would turn out to be in some sense right after all. What is to be said about this in the centenary year of the *Origin of Species*? Did Butler have the best of the argument, and is orthodox Darwinism dead? No perfectly simple answer can be given to these questions. Darwinism, we may certainly say, is not dead; it is more alive than it was fifty years ago—if by Darwinism we mean evolution by natural selection, and all the attitudes associated with that doctrine. Whereas fifty years ago there were biologists who doubted (as indeed Darwin himself had sometimes doubted) whether natural selection alone could ever account for so great a part of the facts of evolutionary change, the most up-to-date schools once again think of it as Darwin did, though with a greatly increased knowledge of its detailed workings.

Darwin himself admitted with chagrin that he could not account for the origin of the variations upon which natural selection has to work. Butler was right to fix on this as the great gap in Darwinian theory, and one cannot blame him (or others who have since done the like) for finding in the Lamarckian concepts of use and disuse, sense of need, and willed effort, the only possible alternative to Darwinism on the one hand, and traditional teleology on the other. Moreover, neither Butler nor any professional scientist of that time was in a position to rule out, on experimental grounds, the possibility of the Lamarckian inheritance of so-called 'acquired characters', on which Lamarck's whole theory hinged.

During the past half-century the science of genetics, taking its cue from Mendelism, has greatly extended our knowledge of what might be called the mechanics of inheritance. Darwin was worried by the thought that the blending of parental characters, carried on for many generations, should theoretically produce standard or average types with little capacity for further variation. Modern genetics has solved this problem by discovering that the genes, or units of heredity, do not blend at all, but, whether in the dominant or the recessive states, remain constant. The continued presence, from generation to generation, of latent or recessive genes maintains the possibility of new genetic departures and combinations. But are we any nearer to knowing what causes the genetic mutations themselves, without which there could be no evolution? Butler was right again, and truly scientific, in not wanting to fall back on 'chance', which after all simply indicates scientific failure. To eliminate chance (or for that matter notions like Lamarck's 'will'), and to substitute demonstration, is the main aim and *raison- d'être* of all science. And, as I understand, it is still the hope of geneticists to find and formulate the laws governing the origin of gene-mutations. At present, they tell us, they can say no more than that natural selection may favour organisms whose gene-structure has a 'tendency to be modified in directions which are useful in dealing with environmental stresses'.[1] 'Tendency' is one of those metaphysical notions which have to be used by science until the exact account is forthcoming; and Dr Wadding-ton states that gene-mutation, or the 'origin of new alleles', must still be regarded as a 'random' process. He adds that natural selection may produce an hereditary constitution in which the right new alleles are likely to appear, and that although the effects of the use or disuse of organs are not inherited directly, they may 'be acted on by natural selection in such a way that they set a stage on which new variations will appear; and set it so that some of these variations will be appropriate for the demands which life is making. Darwin may not have been so wrong as many have since thought him in feeling that there was something—he was never quite sure what—in Lamarck's views.'

If so, we are allowed to say that Butler was not wrong in criticizing Darwin for trying in the first place to dodge Lamarck, and then for not openly enough avowing that he had later been driven, in some degree, to fall back upon him. The situation today seems to be that natural selection remains where Darwin left it, save that it now operates upon a much better understood and much more complex group of factors. Better understood in the manner of its working, yes; but the ultimate cause still eludes analysis. How were these mysterious tendencies imparted

[1] C. H. Waddington, *A Century of Darwin* (1958), p. 17.

to matter or to living genes, so that they do in fact behave in the ways that science can detect? Those who, on other and much wider grounds, find that a religious interpretation of existence is essential to their well-being will not be hampering science if they insist that, however far science may (rightly) push back the frontiers of our ignorance, it can never transcend human limitations or entitle us to dismiss, as an unnecessary hypothesis, the Maker of heaven and earth and of all things visible and invisible.

LECTURE IV

Butler and Religion

IN the preceding lecture I mentioned Butler's view that religion could not be kept out of evolution. In the present lecture I want to consider Butler's attitude to religion more closely, and I will take as my text his description of God in *Luck, or Cunning?* as 'the ineffable contradiction in terms whose presence none can either enter, or ever escape'.[1]

All through his life Butler was vexed by this contradiction; he wanted to escape from God—at least from the God of his father—but he also wanted to enter into God's presence. The dilemma was foreshadowed in that early Darwinian dialogue, when he had said 'I believe in Christianity and I believe in Darwin'. And as Mr Malcolm Muggeridge has said, the reason why 'a haphazard bringing about of variations did not really suit him', was that 'it left out God; and though he wanted God left out in a certain sense, he also wanted Him included.'[2]

There are some well-known aphorisms in Butler's *Note-Books* which are often taken (by those who consider them at all) to embody the very essence of Butlerism. I mean such things as these:

> To love God is to have good health, good looks, good sense, experience, a kindly nature and a fair balance of cash in hand (p. 33).

[1] p. 136.
[2] *The Earnest Atheist* (1936), p. 84.

The good swell is the creature towards which all nature has been groaning and travailing until now. He shows what may be done in the way of good breeding, health, looks, temper and fortune. . . . He preaches the gospel of grace (pp. 35-36).

It is all very well for mischievous writers to maintain that we cannot serve God and Mammon. Granted that it is not easy, but nothing that is worth doing ever is easy. Easy or difficult, possible or impossible, not only has the thing got to be done, but it is exactly in doing it that the whole duty of man consists. And when the righteous man turneth away from his righteousness that he hath committed and doeth that which is neither quite lawful nor quite right, he will generally be found to have gained in amiability what he has lost in holiness (p. 24).[1]

These and many more of Butler's proverbs of hell were exciting when they first appeared, and what gave them added piquancy was that the devil's disciple was citing Scripture to his purpose—that is, inverting it. The identification of love of God with worldly success, of the gospel of grace with physical grace and good fortune, and the preference given to amiability over righteousness—these pleasantly Satanic reversals sent an agreeable *frisson* down the spine. The generation that discovered Butler, which was a generation in revolt against what it called 'Victorianism', found in his oracles precisely the right tone; it found plain-speaking, insight, emancipation from humbug, mockery which was somehow earnest, and blasphemy which was somehow reverent. What a very clever and original man Mr Butler must have been, to be able to prophesy while standing on his head! How witty and

[1] References are to the edition of 1919.

courageous of him to say, for instance, 'An honest God's the noblest work of man'! or of Miss Savage, asking Butler to forgive her for not replying to a letter, to say 'As you are not a Christian perhaps you will.'

This trick of turning phrases and notions upside-down is related to another of Butler's characteristic habits: that of turning things inside-out—or shall we say, expecting insides to correspond to outsides, and feeling cheated when they don't. Of course, he was continually being let down in this way, and that was what made him a satirist and a debunker. The shock of finding that things are not what they seem began for him in boyhood, when, as we read in the Memoir of 'John Pickard Owen' (a largely autobiographical sketch prefacing *The Fair Haven*), he first saw a fowl being trussed, and discovered 'that fowls were not all solid flesh, but that their insides—and these formed, as it appeared to him, an enormous percentage of the bird—were perfectly useless. He was now', he goes on, 'beginning to understand that sheep and cows were also hollow as far as good meat was concerned. . . . What right had they, or anything else, to assert themselves as so big, and prove so empty? . . . The world itself was hollow, made up of shams and delusions, full of sound and fury signifying nothing.'[1] Here is the germ of a satirist's indignation, and one remembers Swift's 'last week I saw a woman flayed, and you will hardly believe how much it altered her person for the worse'. From fowls and sheep the unmasking proceeded to family relations, moral codes, scientific theories, reputations, and at last to Christianity itself. He was puzzled, quite early in life, by

[1] *The Fair Haven* (1913 ed.), pp. 7-8.

the repetition of the General Confession in Church every week: could it be really necessary for good and pious folk to declare, so regularly and so everlastingly, that they were miserable offenders and that there was no health in them? If this were indeed so, what good was their religion doing them? Later, when he was conducting a Sunday class for young people in a London slum, he discovered to his great surprise that one of his favourite pupils had never been baptized:

> He pushed his inquiries further, and found that out of the fifteen boys in his class only five had been baptized, and, not only so, but that no difference in disposition or conduct could be discovered between the regenerate boys and the unregenerate.[1]

This is the realization that underlies the satire on the conversion and baptism of the heathen Chowbok in *Erewhon*. The ironic pose here, it will be remembered, is that the narrator is a pious evangelical:

> I had set my heart upon making him a real convert to the Christian religion. . . . I used to catechize him by our camp fire, and explain to him the mysteries of the Trinity and of original sin, with which I was myself familiar, having been the grandson of an archdeacon by my mother's side, to say nothing of the fact that my father was a clergyman of the English Church. I was therefore sufficiently qualified for the task, and was the more inclined to it, over and above my real desire to save the unhappy creature from an eternity of torture, by recollecting the promise of St James, that if any one converted a sinner (which Chowbok surely was) he should hide a multitude of sins. . . . I baptized him . . . from one of the pannikins (the only vessels I had)

[1] *The Fair Haven* (1913 ed.), p. 17.

reverently, and, I trust, efficiently. I then set myself to work to instruct him in the deeper mysteries of our belief. . . . Chowbok was very hard to teach. Indeed, on the very evening of the same day I baptized him he tried for the twentieth time to steal the brandy, which made me rather unhappy as to whether I could have baptized him rightly.[1]

It is not surprising—it is only what we should have expected—that Butler, having discovered the hollowness of fowls and sheep, of compulsory family affection, and of baptismal regeneration, should turn his quizzical and prosaic eye upon the Christian faith itself. In *The Way of All Flesh*, Ernest Pontifex, during his brief parsonical phase, visits the sceptical tinker Mr Shaw with a view to converting him. Mr Shaw confounds him by asking him to summarize the Resurrection story as given in St John's Gospel. This Ernest cannot do; he mixes up 'the four accounts in a deplorable manner', and Shaw advises him to go home and read these accounts carefully, with attention to the differences between them. Butler himself began a similar comparative study of the Gospels while he was at Cambridge, and went on with it in New Zealand. The effect of this study upon him was the same as that produced upon Ernest Pontifex: 'his belief in the stories concerning the Death, Resurrection and Ascension of Jesus Christ, and hence his faith in all the other Christian miracles . . ., dropped off him once and for ever'.[2] The just, he still believed, shall live by faith; faith, not reason, is the *ultima ratio*. But by what faith shall a just man live in the nineteenth century? 'At any rate not by faith in the

[1] *Erewhon* (1917 ed.), pp. 38-40.
[2] *The Way of All Flesh* (1919 ed.), p. 284.

supernatural element of the Christian religion.' Having discovered that he had been humbugged once again, this time in a matter of such great concern, his first thought was to disabuse his fellow-countrymen. And to Ernest Pontifex it seemed best to start with the Archbishop of Canterbury:

> If he could only manage to sprinkle a pinch of salt, as it were, on the Archbishop's tail, he might convert the whole Church of England to free thought by a *coup de main*. There must be an amount of cogency which even an Archbishop . . . would not be able to withstand. When brought face to face with the facts, as he, Ernest, could arrange them, his Grace would have no resource but to admit them; being an honourable man he would at once resign his Archbishopric, and Christianity would become extinct in England within a few months' time.[1]

Butler is here being ironical at his own expense; he knew, by the time he wrote this passage, that stating 'truths' is not the same thing as winning acceptance for them. But it took him most of his life to learn this.

After his return from New Zealand Butler published anonymously a pamphlet called *The Evidence for the Resurrection of Jesus Christ, as given by the Four Evangelists, critically examined* (1865). This was afterwards worked up in *The Fair Haven* (1873) under the heading 'Difficulties felt by Our Opponents'. I will refer to the latter shortly; for the moment it is enough to note that the discrepancies between the gospel narratives convinced Butler that Jesus never in fact died upon the Cross, and that his later reappearances were real, but mistaken by his followers as

[1] *The Way of All Flesh* (1919 ed.), p. 289.

miraculous. First let us consider briefly what is said in *Erewhon* (1872) about Church and religion.

In the account of the Musical Banks[1] the ambivalence of Butler's attitude to the Church comes out distinctly; he laughs at it and thinks it a fraud, yet he respects it and hankers after it. The Musical Bank currency was treated in *Erewhon* as *the* true currency, and 'all who wished to be considered respectable, kept a larger or smaller balance at these banks'. Yet this currency had no commercial value in the outside world. Even one of the black-gowned bank-attendants (vergers), when offered a tip in the bank currency, 'became so angry that I had to give him a piece of the other kind of money to pacify him'. The Banks, though spoken of everywhere as 'the most precious of all institutions', were generally almost empty, and seemed to be doing very little business. The cashiers and managers (clergy) had an unpleasant appearance and expression; they lacked 'the true Erewhonian frankness'; the look in their faces was not, like that of the High Ydgrunites (gentlemen, men of the world), one to be emulated and diffused. They were indeed mostly good, well-meaning men, and very poorly paid,

> but they had had the misfortune to have been betrayed into a false position at an age for the most part when their judgment was not matured, and after having been kept in studied ignorance of the real difficulties of the system.

The practical neglect of the Banks by the very people who professed to rate them most highly was deplored by the Erewhonians, and one of the Bank Managers explained

[1] *Erewhon*, chap. XV.

to the narrator that something was being done about it. For instance, new stained glass had been put into all the Bank windows; the organs had been enlarged; and the presidents 'had taken to riding in omnibuses and talking nicely to the people in the streets and to remembering the ages of the children, and giving them things when they were naughty. . . .' But as for doing anything to give the currency real value and meaning, this was considered 'not in the least necessary'.

The other side of Butler's attitude, the side that hankered after the Church and hated the new pseudo-religion of science, comes out first in his description of the Bank architecture: it was 'an epic in stone and marble': it 'carried both imagination and judgment by storm'; he was 'charmed and melted'; he felt humbled, made aware of a remote past and of his own insignificance; and reflected that 'the people whose sense of the fitness of things was equal to the upraising of so serene a handiwork, were hardly likely to be wrong in the conclusions they might come to upon any subject'. And then, in one of those passages where Butler drops the allegory and gives us his own opinion in plain terms, he goes on to explain the true *raison d'être* of the Banks: they are a standing witness, he says, to the reality of 'a Kingdom that is not of this world', of which we know nothing 'save that it exists and is powerful'; and of the unseen power to which man 'gives the name of God'.

The Erewhonian Musical Banks, and perhaps the religious systems of all countries, are now more or less of an attempt to uphold the unfathomable and uncon-scious instinctive wisdom of millions of past generations, against the comparatively shallow, consciously reasoning, and ephemeral conclusions drawn from that of the last thirty or forty.

This passage, in spite of its Burkean tone, is to be thought of in relation not to Burke (whom, it is tolerably certain, Butler had not read) but to Butler's notions about unconscious memory in *Life and Habit*. The things we do best of all, such as breathing, are the things of which we are least conscious, because we have done them longest. And similarly with belief in God: this belief is only perfect when held unquestioningly, unconsciously and as a matter of instinctive hereditary wisdom; it withers under rational 'demonstration'. The things we know best are those that we know without knowing that we know them. In this context, Butler characteristically adopts for his own purposes the Christian distinction between Grace and Law: unconscious knowers and believers are under Grace, conscious knowers under Law. The carefree natural man who has 'good health, good looks, good temper, common sense, and energy'—that is, who loves God—is under Grace; he is master of a better science than the earnest scientific discoverers, the professors and the theologians, who are under Law. In a passage which recalls that in *Culture and Anarchy* where Arnold wonders what Shakespeare or Virgil would have thought of the Pilgrim Fathers, Butler invites his readers to look at photographs of eminent men 'literary, artistic, or scientific, and note the work which the consciousness of knowledge has wrought on nine out of every ten of them, and then think of the Venus of Milo, the Discobolus, or the St George of Donatello'. The Church, as we saw, has always stood for 'grace of some sort', in comparison with which mere earthly knowledge is unimportant. 'Her buildings, her music, her architecture, touch us as none other on the whole can do; when she speaks there are many of us who think that she denies the deeper truths of her own profounder mind. The more she gives way to this—the more she becomes conscious of knowing—the less she will know. But still her ideal is in grace.' 'And grace is best, for where grace is, love is not far distant.' Butler was far too self-critical to imagine that he possessed this grace merely because he could write in praise of it:

> In that I write at all [he said] I am among the damned. If [the reader] must believe in anything, let him believe in the music of Handel, the painting of Giovanni Bellini, and in the thirteenth chapter of St Paul's First Epistle to the Corinthians.[1]

It is typical of Butler's slapdash methods, and his lack (in *Erewhon*) of any consistent satiric poise, that the country of Erewhon should be sometimes a topsy-turvy England and at other times a Utopia. Here, for instance, after exposing the humbug of the Musical Banks, he ends by praising them for avoiding the mistake made by 'almost all religions'—that of pretending to know more about the unseen than they possibly can know. In the theological discussion between Higgs (to give him, for convenience, the name he bears in *Erewhon Revisited*) and Arowhena there is a satiric shift of a different kind. Higgs found that the Erewhonians worshipped justice, strength, hope, fear, love, etc., and that they regarded these as gods

[1] *Life and Habit*, pp. 41-2. (See, with reference to the above paragraph, the whole of chap. II.)

having 'a real objective existence in a region far beyond the clouds'. Arowhena maintained that if we did not believe Justice to be 'a beautiful woman . . . with her eyes blinded', holding a pair of scales, we should no longer reverence justice or try to be just. Higgs tries and fails to persuade her that we should go on being just or hopeful even if Justice and Hope were only personifications of human thoughts and feelings. What is more, Arowhena turns the tables on him by asking what if his own God should turn out to be only 'the expression for men's highest conception of goodness, wisdom and power', so that men could love him without believing him to be a person—could, indeed, only properly love 'God' when understanding this word in the 'enlightened' way. Faced with this counter-attack in kind, Higgs immediately ceases to be Butler and becomes the pious and conventional missionary, pointing out to Arowhena that 'we had books whose genuineness was beyond all possibility of doubt, as they were certainly none of them less than 1800 years old, and that these contained authentic accounts of dialogues between men and God'. Is it a satiric inconsistency on Butler's part to use Higgs thus in one short passage, first as the mouthpiece for his own views and immediately afterwards as the object of attack? Not, I think, if Arowhena and Higgs are both meant to illustrate a general human characteristic: open-eyed enlightenment about other people's opinions combined with rigid adherence to our own.

The showing-up of orthodox Christian theology was only an incidental *motif* in *Erewhon*, but it remained Butler's central preoccupation until about 1877, when it began to be superseded by the showing-up of Darwin. His first imperative need was to extricate himself from the bogus religion of Langar Rectory; he must first (in the sense and with the reservations I have tried to indicate) learn to do without God before he could slang Darwin for doing the same. It is not surprising, then, that after publishing *Erewhon* he should write *The Fair Haven* (1873), his most elaborate and sustained attack upon Christianity.

The Fair Haven is an ironical defence of Christianity—specifically of the Resurrection story—which, under the guise of orthodox zeal, undermines its miraculous foundation. Like *Erewhon*, it was first published anonymously, but in *The Fair Haven* Butler carries the mystification a degree further by ascribing the work to 'the late John Pickard Owen' and adding a memoir of the author by his brother 'William Bickersteth Owen'. According to R. A. Streatfeild, the book was not a deliberate hoax; perhaps, however, it would be nearer the truth to say that it was not a hoax and nothing more. Butler seriously hoped to make people study and compare the gospel narratives (as Shaw made Ernest Pontifex do); he hoped to sow, in the minds of many who would never have read an avowedly unorthodox book, doubts about their historical accuracy. But it is also certain that Butler enjoyed the fun of taking in those who were too dense to see through the irony. Why should anyone ever write ironically instead of stating his case in plain terms? Why did Swift write *A Modest Proposal* and *An Argument against abolishing Christianity*? Surely for sheer intellectual pleasure, the joy of creation; and because the oblique method, being a more subtle and controlled form of rhetoric, is far more persuasive than undisguised anger or zeal. In the Preface to the second edition (in which he acknowledged his authorship), Butler, still enjoying himself hugely, gives a further turn to the screw by alleging, as his reason for anonymity, that if *The Fair Haven* had been at once known to proceed from the author of *Erewhon* it might have been suspected of being satirical.

The ostensible plan is to show how John Pickard Owen, after passing through every stage of sceptical doubt, and after considering every possible argument of infidelity, at last reached safe anchorage in the fair haven of orthodox faith. In reality, a very large portion of the book is devoted to stating, with great cogency and detail, the negative side; and although Mr Owen continually assures us that he is only letting the infidels have their say in order to triumph over them at the end, the triumph, when it comes, is as perfunctory as Gulliver's over the King of Brobdingnag—that is to say, it only gives away the case still more completely. It would be tedious, and would nowadays serve no useful purpose, to rehearse the many 'Difficulties felt by our Opponents', or to summarize Butler's reasons for holding that Jesus never actually died upon the Cross, and consequently did not rise from the dead or ascend into heaven. Behind all the analysis of discrepancies in the gospel texts lies the determining pre-supposition, common in the 1870's (when, besides *The Fair Haven*, *Ecce Homo* and *Literature and Dogma* also appeared) that miracles do not happen. The chapters (V-VIII) in which the infidel case is set forth, represent Butler's own view quite directly; they were (as I have said) worked up from his early pamphlet on the evidence for the Resurrection. It may seem extraordinary that any of his first readers should have taken the book seriously as a defence of orthodoxy, yet this did happen. Canon Ainger was completely taken in, and sent a copy of *The Fair Haven* to a friend of Miss Savage 'whom he wished to convert'. *The Rock* newspaper said that 'the work contains many beautiful passages on the discomfort of unbelief, and the holy pleasure of a settled faith, which cannot fail to benefit the reader'. Butler himself thought that his real drift should have been obvious to all but the very stupid; he had even included, in the Memoir of John Pickard Owen, the statement that the late lamented author had gone out of his mind after writing the book.

But even though we may be warier than Canon Ainger or *The Rock*, we may still be puzzled by certain parts of *The Fair Haven*. There are passages, for instance, where Butler seems to be a serious apologist, not indeed for traditional Christianity, but for modernist Christianity; he also appears zealous for a concordat between religion and science. He uses the method of apologetics-by-concession, now favoured by some theologians: that is to say, you concede to the rationalists that many of the old beliefs (formerly thought essential) are untenable, and you expect them in return to abate something of their self-confidence and arrogance. Owen is said to have tried in this way to explain the contending parties to each other; he must show, says the Memoir, that 'Rationalists are right in demurring to the historical accuracy of much that has been too obstinately defended by so-called ortho-dox writers'. This is exactly what the demythologizers do today, and we feel that Butler ought to have meant it seriously himself. But did he? One's confidence that he did is shaken by finding that another part of Owen's task is to prove that Christians are right, on rationalist principles, in clinging to the traditional view of the Resurrection—and this we know to be ironical. He is serious when he says that Christians must not be disingenuous like Dean Alford; we must not pretend that the gospels could be 'harmonized' if we only knew *all* the facts; we must not pretend to be 'sure' of things in the way that science alone can be 'sure'. But what of the following passage:

. . . where, upon the Christian side, was the attempt to grapple with the real difficulties now felt by unbelievers? Simply nowhere. . . . Modern Christianity seemed to shrink from grappling with modern Rationalism, and displayed a timidity which could not be accounted for except by the supposition of a secret misgiving that certain things were being defended which could not be defended fairly. This was quite intolerable; a misgiving was a warning voice from God, which should be attended to as a man valued his soul. On the other hand, the conviction reasonably entertained by unbelievers that they were right on many not inconsiderable details of the dispute, and that so-called orthodox Christians in their hearts knew it but would not own it—or that if they did not know it they were only in ignorance because it suited their purpose to be so—this conviction gave an overweening self-confidence to infidels, as though they must be right in the whole because they were so in part; they therefore blinded themselves to all the more fundamental arguments in support of Christianity because certain shallow ones had been put forward in the front rank, and been far too obstinately defended.[1]

[1] *The Fair Haven*, pp. 57-8.

How familiarly this reads! It might easily occur in a twentieth-century course of Gifford or Hibbert Lectures, or in a history of the Victorian science-and-religion controversy by a sensible and impartial modern Christian. Ought not Butler to have meant every word of this? Can he really be scoffing at the very idea of reconciliation, and satirizing the notion that when all is conceded that the rationalists could legitimately desire, the 'fundamentals' of Christianity still remain? Everything depends, of course on what the 'fundamentals' are taken to be. The modernist apologetic-by-concession, from Jowett to the present time, has always presupposed that *something* fundamental remains undamaged, whether it be the mystery of the Incarnation, the example of Christ's life and teaching, the existence and vitality of the Church, the facts of spiritual experience, the Christian character and ethic, or a combination of such elements. Butler, we may agree, is satirizing this very method in so far as the fundamental to be presupposed is the Resurrection, or indeed any of the Christian miracles. His irony glances sharply upon the trick of making concessive gestures without really making any important concession at all:

> Suppose we were driven to admit that nothing in the life of our Lord can be certainly depended upon beyond the facts that He was begotten of the Holy Ghost of the Virgin Mary; that He worked many miracles upon earth, and delivered St Matthew's version of the sermon on the mount and most of the parables as we now have them; finally, that He was crucified, dead, and buried, that He rose again from the dead upon the third day, and ascended unto [*sic*] Heaven. Granting for the sake of argument that we could rely on no

other parts, what would follow? Nothing which could in any way impair the living power of Christianity.[1]

We know that Butler's aim was to disprove the miracles by the oblique method of letting the infidels state their case and then silencing them ineffectually. But what are we to make of the following:

> The Christ-ideal which, after all, is the soul and spirit of Christianity would remain precisely where it was, while its recognition would be far more general, owing to the departure on the part of its apologists from certain lines of defence which are irreconcilable with the ideal itself.

Is this ironical? He goes on:

> After all, it is not belief in the facts which constitutes the essence of Christianity, but rather the being so impregnated with love at the contemplation of Christ that imitation becomes almost instinctive; this it is which draws the hearts of men to God the Father, far more than any intellectual belief that God sent our Lord into the world, ordaining that he should be crucified and rise from the dead. Christianity is addressed rather to the infinite spirit of man than to his finite intelligence, and the believing in Christ through love is more precious in the sight of God than any loving through belief.[2]

Where is the catch here? This seems to be straight modernism of the Jowett type—the more so as it is out of character in the mouth of John Pickard Owen, who is supposed to hold that belief in the basic 'facts' (the Resurrection and Ascension) *is* essential. I suppose the rather unctuous tone, which is not that of Butler's natural speaking-voice,

[1] *The Fair Haven*, p. 234-5.   [2] *ibid.*, p. 248.

should be a sufficient danger-signal; but I must own that when I read the Chapter called 'The Christ Ideal' (Chapter IX) I was taken in by it—at least to the extent of thinking that Butler really clung to some such residuum as this. I was therefore comforted to find the following in Festing Jones's *Memoir*—part of a note made by Butler in 1885 about a conversation with the Reverend E. A. Abbott (an old College acquaintance).

> Abbott said: 'And did you really mean none of that part seriously?'
> I said: 'Certainly not; I intended it as an example of the kind of rubbish which would go down with *The Spectator*.'
> Abbott said: 'Well, I can only say you would have found a great many to sympathize with you, if you had meant it seriously.'
> I said, rather drily: 'That, I think, is exceedingly probable,'
> meaning that there was no lack of silly insincere gushers. Abbott did not see what I meant, and we parted genially.[1]

Abbott, it is illuminating to note, was the author of a book showing 'that a believer in evolution may remain a believer in natural Christianity unassailable by science; and that one who may be unable to accept the miracles of the Bible as historical may nevertheless retain his faith in the Incarnation, the Atonement, the Spiritual Resurrection of Christ, and the Doctrine of the Trinity'. If one could understand why Butler disliked this kind of modernism one would have the clue to his rather labyrinthine thought. He ought, perhaps we feel, to have

[1] *Memoir*, vol. I, p. 182. Abbot was the brother of Jowett's biographer.

approved of a restatement of Christian doctrine (such as Mr Abbott's) which would be acceptable both to Christians and to evolutionists? Not a bit: he appears here to regard it in much the same way as Frederic Harrison regarded *Essays and Reviews*, namely as parsonical humbug —an attempt to have the best of both worlds, to stay in the Church while thinking the thoughts of those more honest men who had left it. There might be, and in fact there was, much in both the Church and in Christianity which Butler could respect and accept; but for him it was essential, first, to come out from among them and be separate. To wear the Hebrew Old Clothes outwardly unchanged but with a new silver lining of modernist meanings, was to him a contemptible piece of Hanky-Panky. Morever, it shook one's self-complacency at having had the courage to reject Christianity altogether.

Through Butler's ironic use of the traditional argument that Christianity could never have originated and spread if it had been founded upon delusion, there comes the impression that in his view it *was* so founded, and that organized Christianity is a vast imposture. 'It is', he wrote in 1887, 'against superstition, and more especially the Christian superstition, that I have fought to the best of my ability.'[1] And yet, a few months later, we find him writing to another correspondent[2] as follows (it is a passage so important that I must quote it at some length):

> Do you—does any man of science—believe that the present orthodox faith can descend many generations longer without modification? Do I—does any free-

[1] *ibid.*, vol. II, p. 49 (to Mrs Heatherley).
[2] Mr Blunt; *ibid.*, p. 53.

thinker who has the ordinary feelings of an Englishman —doubt that the main idea underlying and running through the orthodox faith is substantially sound?

That there is an unseen life and unseen Kingdom which is not of this world, and that the wisdom of this world is foolishness with God; that the life we live here is much but, at the same time, small as compared with another larger life in which we all share though, while here, we can know little if anything about it; that there is an omnipresent Being into whose presence none can enter and from whose presence none can escape—an ineffable contradiction in terms (as I have said in *Luck, or Cunning?*); that the best are still unprofitable servants and that the wisest are still children—who that is in his senses can doubt these things? And surely they are more the essence of Christianity than a belief that Jesus Christ died, rose from the dead, and ascended visibly into heaven.

Technically and according to the letter, of course, they are not. According to the spirit I firmly believe they are. Tell me that Jesus Christ died upon the cross, and I find not one tittle of evidence worthy of the name to support the assertion. Tell me that therefore we are to pull down the Church and turn everyone to his own way, and I reject this as fully as I reject the other. I want the Church as much as I want free-thought; but I want the Church to pull her letter more up to date or else to avow more frankly that her letter is a letter only. If she would do this I, for one, would not quarrel with her. Unfortunately, things do not seem moving in the direction in which I would gladly see them go and do all in my power to help them go.

What separates this from the modernist accommodation demolished by Butler's own irony in *The Fair Haven*? The tone, yes; blunt plain-speaking here, ecclesiastical soapiness there. But what matters more, fourteen years of tilting against the satanic mills of Darwinism, during which Butler had come to realize that his deepest loyalties were on the side of the angels. What Butler said of his own book *Luck, or Cunning?* could be said of himself:

> its very essence is to insist on the omnipresence of mind and intelligence throughout the universe to which no name can be so fittingly applied as God. Orthodox the book is not, religious I do verily believe and hope it is; its whole scope is directed against the present mindless, mechanical, materialistic view of nature and though I know very well that churchmen will not like it, I am sure they will like it much better than the opinions now most generally accepted, and that they will like it much better than men of science will.[1]

Another statement of Butler's faith—of what he took to be the 'kernel' of Christianity, is this:

> faith in an unseen world, in doing one's duty, in speaking the truth, in finding the true life in others rather than in oneself, in the certain hope that he who loses his life on these behalfs finds more than he has lost. What can Agnosticism do against such a Christianity as this? I should be shocked if anything I had ever written or shall ever write should seem to make light of these things.[2]

To which one reply would be, I suppose, that of course Agnosticism could do nothing against this kind of Christianity, because it is not Christianity.

Butler professed to believe that all things work together for good to them that love God, and he believed that he himself loved God in some sense—and perhaps not merely

[1] To Mrs Taylor, October 17, 1886; *Memoir*, vol. II, p. 41.
[2] Quoted by Streatfeild, Introduction to the *The Fair Haven*.

in the sense indicated by the extract quoted at the beginning of this lecture. He believed, like Ernest Pontifex, in 'something as yet but darkly known which makes right right and wrong wrong'. But his explicit theology, as set forth in the book *God the Known and God the Unknown* (originally a series of articles in *The Examiner*, 1879; edited in book form by Streatfeild, 1909) is hardly more satisfactory than Comte's. Instead of deifying Humanity, he deifies all living creatures, all Life, the Life Force. There is no meaning, he says, in the idea of a God who is not a living person; 'an impersonal God is as much a contradiction in terms as an impersonal person'. Where are we to find this person? There is no harm in using the word 'God' to mean the personification of 'our own highest ideal of power, wisdom and duration', but a personification (as Arowhena had pointed out) is not a person. 'God is', he concludes, 'the animal and vegetable world, and the animal and vegetable world is God', a vast leviathan, composed of all living creatures as the body is composed of cells. What then of the mineral Kingdom— is this no part of the Kingdom of God? This very question afterwards occurred to Butler, and he realized that he could not logically deny 'life' to every material particle in the universe. He meant to rewrite the articles on this new assumption, but never did so. If all life is God, the whole universe is the living God, and mind is omnipresent. The Life Everlasting is life in this God—the life still being lived now, for instance, by Bellini or Handel.

This, then, is 'God the Known'. But Butler goes on to ask, what can this 'panzoism' tell us of the origin of matter, or of the primordial life-cell? The world was made and prepared to receive life; hence there must have been a 'designer', 'some far vaster Person who looms out behind our God'. If so 'we are members indeed of the God of this world, but we are not his children; we are children of the Unknown and Vaster God who called him into existence'. Butler's God, then, is not only composed of material units, but is himself a unit in an unknown and vaster personality who is composed of Gods. This is 'God the Unknown'. It is remarkable that Butler, having reduced God to 'all life considered as a whole', goes on to bring in—almost as an afterthought —this super-God who really is transcendent, and who has designed the world and the World-Gods. To which is our worship and reverence due? He says in one place that his World-God, being living and visible, can be believed in, loved, and devotedly served; it is presumably to him, then, that we are in duty bound. But this God lacks the numinous quality of the Super-God; he has no power to inspire reverence or demand service. In Butler there is, as far as I can discover, little or no sense of the holy, and (in spite of his praise of I Corinthians xiii) very little love.

Not long after writing *Erewhon*—and we may safely suppose it to have been while writing *The Fair Haven*— it occurred to Butler to wonder what effect would have been produced upon the Erewhonians by the apparently miraculous escape of Higgs at the end of the story: his ascent into heaven in a balloon with an earthly bride. He decided that to a people like the Erewhonians, who were losing grip on their own official faith, such an event would appear to be an authentic miracle, and would serve as the nucleus of a new religion. What an opportunity he had thus unwittingly given himself to satirize Christianity again! It was too good to miss, but he knew that he must wait for at least twenty years to give the new religion time to take shape. Actually it was nearly thirty years before Butler published *Erewhon Revisited* (1901).

It will be remembered that when Higgs revisits Erewhon he finds that he has been deified as the 'Sunchild', and that Sunchildism, the new cult based upon his ascension, has become the established religion of the country, complete with churches, scriptures (his own sayings and doings, garbled, glossed and swollen with accretions), priesthood and theological professors. The balloon has become a horse-drawn chariot, and there is even a sacred relic (dung alleged to have fallen from the horses). Higgs's moral problem is whether to risk his own life, and risk destroying Sunchildism, by publicly declaring his identity. It is, I think, unnecessary to analyse this book in any detail. The allusion to the rise of any supernatural religion, Christianity included, is obvious. 'If', says Butler 'there be a single great, and apparently well-authenticated miracle, others will accrete round it; then, in all religions that have so originated, there will follow temples, priests, rites, sincere believers and unscrupulous exploiters of public credulity.'[1]

The prosaic, eighteenth-century, Gibbonian part of Butler, still active in his last years, greatly relished exposing the natural growth of a myth, and perhaps even more the hanky-panky of the theologians in darkening counsel and sophisticating the evidence. But Butler went out of his way to explain that he did not mean to poke fun at

[1] *Erewhon Revisited* (reprint of 1920), Preface, p. vi.

Christianity, and still less to suggest any allusion to its Founder; he only meant, he said, to suggest a parallelism 'between the circumstances that would almost inexorably follow such a supposed miracle as the escape of the Sun-child, and those which all who think as I do believe to have accreted round the supposed miracle, not of the Ascension, but of the Resurrection'.[1] The satire is great fun, but the most interesting point in *Erewhon Revisited* is that, after showing up all the imposture, Butler still wants to preserve institutional Sunchildism. This reflects his hankering, which grew upon him with advancing years, for reconciliation with the Church. In the Preface to *Erewhon Revisited* he declares, rather surprisingly to some readers, that he has never ceased to profess himself 'a member of the more advanced wing of the English Broad Church'. 'What those who belong to this wing believe, I believe. What they reject, I reject.' And he endorses, as acceptable to such people, the advice given by Higgs to the Erewhonians after the secret is out. Assuming, as I do, that this passage represents Butler's mature view of what should be done with the Church now that its miracles have been exploded, I will conclude with a short account of it.

At the Mayor's dinner-party, after the dénouement, Dr Downie (Broad Church) says: 'And now Mr Higgs, tell us, as a man of the world, what are we to do about Sunchildism?' The counsel of perfection, Higgs replies, would be make a clean breast of the whole affair, declare publicly who and what he is, and admit the whole vast

---

[1] Letter to Mrs Fuller Maitland, February 10, 1901 (*Memoir*, vol. II, p. 338).

mistake. But this would never do, says Dr Downie; things have gone too far. What would the leaders of the English Church do if they found themselves in the same plight as the Musical Bank managers? This is Higgs's answer:

> Our religion sets before us an ideal which we all cordially accept, but it also tells us of marvels like your chariot and horses, which we most of us reject. Our best teachers insist on the ideal, and keep the marvels in the background. . . . Roughly, then, if you cannot abolish me altogether, make me a peg on which to hang all your own best ethical and spiritual conceptions.

They must, he says, get rid of that wretched relic and other crudities, 'let the cock-and-bull stories' tacitly drop, and invent no new ones. If they will do this, 'I really cannot see why I should not do for you as well as any one else'.

> Your Musical Bank people [he goes on] bear witness to the fact that beyond the Kingdoms of this world there is another, within which the writs of this world's Kingdoms do not run. This is the great service which our Church does for us in England, and hence many of us uphold it, though we have no sympathy with the party now dominant within it. 'Better', we think, 'a corrupt church than none at all.' Moreover, those who in my country would step into the church's shoes are as corrupt as the church, and more exacting.[1]

'Then', says Higgs's son George, 'you would have us uphold Sunchildism, knowing it to be untrue?' Higgs replies:

> Do what you will, you will not get perfect truth. And if you will follow the lead which I believe Dr Downie

[1] *Erewhon Revisited*, pp. 278-81.

will give you, that is to say, get rid of cock-and-bull stories, idealise my unworthy self, and . . . make me a peg on which to hang your own best thoughts— Sunchildism will be as near truth as anything you are likely to get. But if Hankyism triumphs [this means, Butler has explained, everything that we understand by Jesuitry], come what may you must get rid of it, for he and his school will tamper with the one sure and everlasting word of God revealed to us by human experience. He who plays fast and loose with this is as one who would forge God's signature to a cheque drawn on God's own Bank.[1]

[1] *ibid.*, p. 290.

INDEX

(of names other than those of Darwin and Butler)

Abbott, Rev. E. A., 104-5
Agassiz, 21
Ainger, Canon, 100
Alford, Dean, 101
Anaxagoras, 35
Anaximander, 34
Anaximenes, 34
Aquinas, 33, 38-9, 50-1
Argyll, Duke of, 28
Aristotle, 35-7, 50
Arnold, Matthew, 95
Augustine, St., 29, 32, 33, 38-9
Avicenna, 51

Bacon, 39, 40-1
Barlow, Lady N., 74
Basil, St., 50
Birrell, Augustine, 61
Bonnet, C., 42
Bowen, F. (*N. American Review*), 51-3
Buffon, 32, 43-6, 75-6
Burke, 95
Butler, Dr. S. (Headmaster of Shrewsbury), 9, 66-7

Cannon, Prof. H. Graham, 46-7
Carlyle, 42
Carpenter, W. B., 54
Colenso, 9

Copernicus, 29
Cuvier, 21

Darwin, Erasmus, 21, 32, 43-46, 75-9
Democritus, 35
Descartes, 51
Dunns, Rev., 49

Eliot, George, 27
Empedocles, 35, 36
Epicurus, 20, 37

Fawcett, H., 54
Fordyce, J., 28

Geddes, P., 16
Gibbon, 63
Goethe, 42
Goodwin, Bishop Harvey, 82
Gosse, Edmund, 56
Gosse, P. H., 55-9

Haeckel, 41
Harrison, F., 105
Heraclitus, 34
Herder, 41-2
Herschel, 10
Hooker, J. D., 11-12, 56
Humboldt, 10
Huxley, T. H., 33-4, 48, 51, 57, 79, 81

Jaeger, W., 36
Jones, H. Festing, 61, 74
Jowett, B., 102

Kant, 41
Kingsley, C., 19-20, 59
Krause, Dr., 78-9

Lamarck, 21, 32, 43-7, 52,
  60, 75-8, 83-5
Lankester, E. Ray, 79
Leibniz, 41
Linnaeus, 21, 39, 43
Lucretius, 21, 37
Lyell, 11-12, 56

Malthus, 14-17
Maupertuis, 42
Mill, J. S., 55
Milton, 39-40
Mivart, St. G., 53, 72, 74,
  81, 82
Monboddo, Lord, 65
Moore, Aubrey, 20, 31, 39,
  40
Muggeridge, Malcolm, 87

Newman, J. H., 29
Newton, 29, 54

Owen, Sir R. (*Edinburgh
  Review*), 51

Paley, 10, 16, 18, 23, 35, 63,
  74
Pascal, 31, 51

Powell, Baden, 54, 58
Pusey, Dr. E. B., 20, 29-30,
  32, 38-9, 49, 52

Rambler, The, 50
Ray, 39, 43
Reddie, J., 56

Saturday Review, 54
Savage, Miss, 82, 89, 100
Schelling, 42
Sedgwick, Adam, 53-4, 57
Shaftesbury, Earl of, 55
Shaw, G. B., 47, 60-1, 62-3
Spencer, Herbert, 16, 77-8
Swift, 89, 98

Thales, 34
Thomson, J. A., 15-17
Tyndall, 78, 81

Vestiges of Creation, 21, 33, 52
Victoria Institute, 55

Waddington, Dr. C. H., 85
Wallace, A. R., 12, 16
Wellington (N.Z.), Bishop
  Abraham of, 65
Wilberforce, Samuel, 20, 48-
  49
Wordsworth, 14, 18

Xenophanes, 34

Yeats, J. B., 63